ELECTRONICS

The science of electronics has revolutionized science and industry. It is bringing ever wider and faster changes. Computers can digest masses of statistics almost on the instant, or perform mathematical calculations with breathtaking speed. Electronic devices can soar with space vehicles through unimaginable distances, can probe and examine and send back pictures and reports from outer space. Everywhere electronics is at work—for example, in medicine, building, accountancy, metallurgy, telecommunications, manufacturing, industry—calculating, checking, testing, stopping, starting, watching and carrying out many other functions.

Reading and understanding this guide will provide a good starting point for anybody with a desire to know more about the theory and application of electronics.

A
GROSSET
ALL-COLOR GUIDE

ELECTRONICS

BY ROLAND WORCESTER
Illustrated by Design Productions

GROSSET & DUNLAP
A NATIONAL GENERAL COMPANY
Publishers • New York

THE GROSSET ALL-COLOR GUIDE SERIES
SUPERVISING EDITOR . . . GEORG ZAPPLER

Board of Consultants

CONTENTS

INTRODUCTION: OUR ELECTRONIC WORLD

Electronics is the tool of today. It has given us radar, automation, space vehicles, radio telescopes and a host of other inventions that have transformed our lives.

Electronics means putting electrons to work. An electron is one of the particles in an atom, and it travels at incredible speed around the nucleus. Also of great importance are the facts that the electron has a negative charge and the nucleus has a positive charge.

Many devices are explained in this book. For example, transformers couple circuits, transform or change one voltage to another or perform other useful functions. Resistors and other circuit elements are described with electronic circuit diagrams which readily show the essential information about a piece of equipment. Again, a transistor is a device made from semiconductor material (e.g., a tiny slice of germanium or silicon). It allows a small current (between base and emitter) to control a large current (between emitter and collector). It is used in television, in computers and in many other devices.

Electronics for entertainment: television, radio, tape recorder.

In cathode ray tubes, an electron beam is deflected by electric or magnetic fields and passes over the face of the tube. These tubes are employed in television receivers, oscilloscopes and other equipment.

Electronic devices can send us information from satellites and space vehicles. Radio telescopes scan the heavens, gathering information from distances far beyond the range of visual observation.

Radar bounces radio signals off distant objects and uses the echo to give information on their distance and direction. Sonar in ships uses sound-wave echoes for depth sounding.

Solar cells produce current when they are illuminated, giving power for space instruments. Light-sensitive diodes and transistors respond to light-pulses, and they control electrical circuits by light. Other diodes produce light under the influence of an electric current. In fact, the skill of the electronics engineer makes of electrons in motion an almost magic tool. And there are still many exciting challenges to be met as he carries on his research and devises fresh applications.

5

BASIC ELECTRICITY

Electrons in Motion

We can make a picture of an atom as simple or as complicated as we like. We can show a hydrogen atom as a central nucleus or proton, circled by a single electron [1]. The proton has a positive charge, and is 1,840 times the mass of the electron, which has a negative charge.

The electron circles the nucleus millions of times in a millionth of a second, and hundreds of millions of atoms side by side would be needed to occupy an inch of space. Positive and negative charges (proton and electron) neutralize each other.

Helium has two electrons and two protons. The heavier elements have more and more electrons [2]. Uranium has 92.

There are other particles besides protons and electrons. The neutron is also found in some atoms. It has no charge; however, it is the 'glue' that holds the proton mass together. Other transitory particles arise, change their state, or apparently disappear in energy.

A hydrogen atom electron can absorb a photon or light particle, and take energy from it, moving to an orbit at a higher energy level. Or electrons may collapse to lower energy levels, emitting photons.

Ions

We have seen that, normally, the negative electron charge equals the positive nucleus charge: hence the atom is in equilibrium. However, sometimes an atom may gain an electron and then it becomes a negative ion. If an atom loses an electron, it becomes a positive ion. With semiconductors, we may speak of positive 'holes' or hole carriers. These can be imagined as spaces which could be occupied by negative electrons.

A body with a considerable excess of electrons has a strong negative charge; one with a relative lack of electrons has

6

a strong positive charge [3]. Thus there is a difference of potential, which exists so long as there is no means of electrons escaping, or nuclei gaining the electrons they lack.

Electrons, being negative, repel one another when they are close together, but are attracted by positive nuclei. A force draws the one to the other. If they are supplied to a *conductor* that allows electrons to move, the force draws them along the conductor to a positive ion region lacking electrons [4]. The force is electromotive force (e.m.f.) and the movement is current.

The Electric Current
If the flow of electrons is to be maintained, a supply must be generated or produced to replace those traveling away from the supply along the conductor. In a circuit, current will flow from the negative battery terminal (supply), along the conductor to a lamp or other apparatus (the load). The electrons that have not been dropped across the load will return along another conductor back to the positive battery terminal.

A supply of electrons can be produced chemically by a

1. Simple picture of a hydrogen atom.

2. Heavier atoms have more electrons.

3. Potential differences between charges of dissimilar polarity.

4. Negative electrons flowing to influence the positive charge.

battery, electromagnetically by a generator or by several other methods.

Conductors

We use conductors to take current to the point where it is wanted. A conductor readily allows the exchange of free orbital electrons, so electrons forming the electric current can move from atom to atom in the material [5]. Silver and copper are good conductors, for they allow current to flow freely. Copper is drawn into wires, or wound into coils or used to carry current [6].

conducting material ⌐

5. Easy exchange of electrons forms current.

6. We take currents where needed by using conductors.

lamp

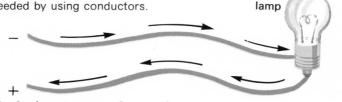

–

+

To find resistance of a conductor:

$$R = \frac{kl}{A}$$

where R =   Resistance
      k =   Material constant
      l =   Length of wire
      A =   Cross-sectional area
              (usually in circular mils)

8

insulation

wire

7. Insulated covering on wires.

insulators supporting
conducting parts

8. Rigid insulating parts.

Insulators

Some materials are poor conductors. This fact makes them
good insulators. A perfect insulator would allow no exchange
of electrons. Hence there would be no movement from atom
to atom, and no current would flow. Pyrex, micalex and
steatite are good insulators, but so are many other substances.
Rubber, polyvinyl chloride (pvc), cotton, silk, enamel or
other insulating material on wires prevents the wires touching
each other or nearby metal parts where current is not wanted
[7].

Glass, mica, ceramic, phenolic plastic and other rigid
insulating parts support conducting items in switches,
tube sockets, transistors, capacitors and many other electronic
components [8].

What is the best kind of insulator depends on the work
it must do. Insulators on wires may need to be thin and
flexible. Insulating parts may have to be very strong or
may have to withstand high voltages or high temperatures.

9

9. Simple cell generates electromotive force chemically.

e.m.f.

+   −

carbon   zinc

solution of electrolyte

10. Popular dry cell

paste sal-ammoniac

zinc can   +   carbon rod

Primary Cells

We said that a potential difference can be produced chemically. Primary cells or batteries do this. If zinc and carbon plates are placed in a solution of sal-ammoniac [9] this happens. Chlorine atoms in the sal-ammoniac take incomplete atoms from the zinc, but each atom removed leaves two electrons. An available supply of electrons, or negative charge, distributes evenly on the zinc plate.

The removed zinc atoms enter the solution as positive ions, or atoms lacking some electrons, until the solution can accept no more. The solution then has a positive charge and so has the carbon plate immersed in contact with it.

A potential difference or electromotive force (e.m.f.) now exists between the zinc and carbon plates. If a wire is connected from zinc to carbon, electrons flow through it. Chemical action maintains surplus electrons at the zinc until the cell is discharged.

The popular 'dry' Leclanché cell has a zinc canister as negative electrode and central carbon rod as the positive [10]. The rod is surrounded by powdered carbon and manganese dioxide, whose molecules can combine with hydrogen molecules to produce water and prevent hydrogen accumulating. The e.m.f. is about 1.5 volts.

Batteries

If the cell is large, there is more area for chemical action, and a more powerful current is available. If cells have the carbon rods and also the zinc cases joined [11], this is electrically like a larger cell. Voltage is that of a single cell.

If cells are joined positive to negative, the cells are in series [12]. The battery voltage is that of the cells added together—3 volts for two 1.5 volt cells, and so on. A layer battery [12] has flat units placed one upon another. Miniature mercury cells are made for small apparatus.

Secondary cells or lead acid cells are re-charged by passing direct current through them from a generator or other supply. A car battery usually has spongy lead and lead peroxide plates in dilute sulphuric acid, and each cell has an e.m.f. of 2 volts. Six cells form a 12 volt battery.

11. A battery can have cells in parallel.

1·5V

6V

layer battery

— cells

12. Cells in series provide a higher voltage.

13. Attraction of dissimilar charges.

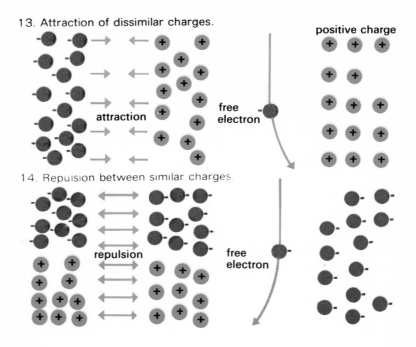

14. Repulsion between similar charges.

Free Electrons

Negative electrons move toward a positive charge [13]. If a free electron is moving near a positive charge, its path is curved, because of this attraction.

Repulsion exists between charges of the same polarity [4]. The path of a free electron or stream of electrons curves away from a negative charge. These effects are used to direct the electron stream in various electronic devices, such as the cathode ray tube used in oscilloscopes. The path of a free electron is also changed by a magnetic field. Television tubes and magnetrons utilize this effect.

Electron Gun

A stream of electrons is obtained from an electron gun having a cathode heated by an internal filament [15]. The high temperature causes thermionic emission of electrons. The beam passes through a hole in a cylinder, its intensity controlled by potential applied. Making the cylinder negative repels electrons and reduces the beam.

15. Electron gun emits stream of electrons.

Focusing

A convex optical lens will focus light rays to a point. An electron lens has a similar effect on the cathode ray beam, the electric field curvature acting in much the same way as the glass lens on light rays [16]. Cylinders having different potentials have a similar effect.

By controlling the potential on one or more electrodes, the intensity of the field and its curvature can be adjusted to focus the stream of electrons into a narrow beam.

The cathode ray tube has an electron gun, grid or aperture to control beam intensity, and accelerator and focusing electrodes. The beam strikes a fluorescent coating, producing a spot of light visible on the tube. Stray electrons are absorbed by the aquadag coating.

16 Focusing the beam in a cathode ray tube

13

17. Voltage = pressure

18. Current flowing is in amperes

Circuit Laws and Units

A volt (V) is the unit of *pressure* from a battery or from some other source. A dry cell has a pressure of 1.5 volts. Two cells in series provide 1.5 + 1.5 = 3 volts. A vessel half full has a depth of water H1 [17]. The depth H2 is twice H1. A pipe from the bottom of the second vessel delivers water at twice the pressure of the first vessel. Similarly, raising the voltage increases electrical pressure.

Some circuits operate at low voltage. Others require hundreds or thousands of volts. 1,000 volts = 1 kilovolt, or 1kV. On the other hand, very low voltages are in millivolts or mV. 1,000mV = 1V. Extremely low voltages are in microvolts, or μV. 1,000μV = 1mV.

The ampere (A) is the unit of current flow. For example, a bulb could take 1A [18a]. Two such bulbs take 1 ampere each, or 2 amperes, or twice as much current [18b].

Small currents are given in milliamperes, or mA. 1,000 mA = 1 ampere. Extremely small currents are in microamperes, or μA. 1,000μA = 1mA.

The ohm (Ω) is the unit of *resistance*. A thick wire has little resistance and lets current pass readily [19]. In the same way a large pipe lets water flow easily. A thin wire resists the ready flow of current, just as the small pipe offers resistance to the flow of water. The greater the electrical resistance of a component or circuit, the more the passage of current is hindered.

Copper wires have little resistance, so they let current pass readily. But we may want resistance in many circuits. Iron and alloy wires can provide this. Making the wire thinner or increasing its length raises the resistance. Carbon compounds resist the ready flow of current, and can be formed into rods having any resistance needed. They are widely used. A component having resistance is a *resistor* [20]. A variable resistor has a sliding contact, bringing into circuit as much of the resistance element as is wanted. A potentiometer has a connection at each end and sliding contact.

For high values we use kΩ, k, or kilo-ohm. 1k = 1,000 ohms. Very high values are in MΩ (megohms). 1 MΩ = 1,000k. Resistors are usually color-coded. Each color shows a figure, or a number of zeros.

19. Ohm = unit of resistance

thick wire

large pipe

thin wire

small pipe

20. Resistors and color codes

wire wound resistor

1st figure
2nd figure
No. of zeros } =56,000 Ω

circuit symbol

color-coded carbon resistors

2·2 MΩ

Gold=5%
potentiometer

black		0
brown		1
red		2
orange		3
yellow		4
green		5
blue		6
violet		7
gray		8
white		9

color   code

variable resistors

knob

carbon track

15

Ohm's Law

If we increase the voltage applied to a circuit, the electron flow becomes stronger [21]. Reducing the voltage makes the current weaker.

If we leave the voltage the same, increasing the resistance will make the current weaker [22]. Reducing the resistance naturally allows more current to flow.

These facts are the basis of Ohm's Law. We say:

Current in Amperes × *Resistance in Ohms* = e.m.f. As *I* is used for current, and *R* for ohms, this is $I \times R = E$, or $IR = E$. In the same way, $\dfrac{E}{I} = R$ and $\dfrac{E}{R} = I$.

Always remember that the basic units are amperes, volts and ohms. As an example, 1mA flows through 100k. What voltage is dropped? 1mA = 0.001 ampere, and 100k = 100,000 ohms. So 0.001 × 100,000 = 100 volts.

The *power* that is usefully employed or perhaps wasted or dissipated as heat in a circuit is given in watts. Useful power could raise the temperature of tube heaters, or operate a loudspeaker or other device. Wasted power might be that lost in a resistor which is used to drop the voltage.

21. Current increases with voltage.

22. Increasing resistance reduces current.

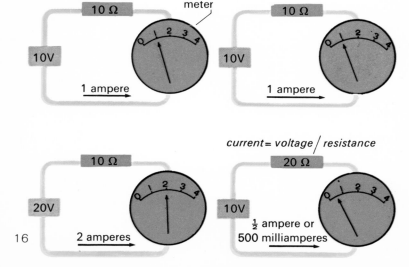

meter

10 Ω
10V
1 ampere

10 Ω
10V
1 ampere

current = voltage / resistance

10 Ω
20V
2 amperes

20 Ω
10V
½ ampere or
500 milliamperes

16

36 watt bulb

12V

3 amperes

23. Electrical power in a circuit (Power = watts = voltage × current).

A

400 Ω ¼ watt

10V

25mA

B

100V +

8000 Ω

0.8W

20V+

2000 Ω

0.2W

−

24. Voltage, resistance, current and wattage.

We could give the useful output of an amplifier or other device in watts. Small powers are given in milliwatts. 1,000 mW = 1 watt. Power in watts = voltage × current.

Voltage in Volts × Current in Amperes = Power in Watts

Or we can say $\dfrac{Watts}{Volts} = Amperes$ or $\dfrac{Watts}{Amperes} = Volts$

A 36 watt car bulb is run from a 12 volt battery [23]. So it draws $\dfrac{36}{12} = 3$ amperes current.

Imagine that a potential of 10 volts is present across a 400 ohm resistor [24a].

From $I = \dfrac{Volts}{Resistance} = \dfrac{10}{400} = 0.025$ ampere.

With resistors in series, 8,000 ohms + 2,000 ohms = 10,000 ohms [24b]. From $I = \dfrac{E}{R}$ or $\dfrac{100}{10,000}$ we find that 10mA (0.01A) flows.

17

The Inductor

The inductor is a wire wound as a coil. When current is applied, a magnetic field swells around the coil. When the coil is disconnected, a spark appears between the disconnected lead and the source, and the magnetic field collapses. These events indicate that energy had been stored in the coil field.

Both the building and collapsing fields resist changes in current flow (show *reactance*). With a current alternately changing back and forth, or *alternating current* (AC), the inductor assumes an inductive reactance that acts much like a resistance [25a]. The more turns on the coil, the more its inductance and the more its reactance [25b].

The formula $X_L = 2\pi fL$ gives reactance where:

$$X_L^{\cdot} = \quad \text{Reactance in ohms}$$
$$2\pi = \quad \text{Constant for one cycle}$$
$$f = \quad \text{Frequency in Hertz (Hz)}$$
$$L = \quad \text{Inductance in henrys}$$

In Figure 26A the supply has a frequency of 50 cycles per second, or 50 Hz. It changes direction 50 times a second. At [26b] the frequency is 100 Hz. The reactance of the inductor B is twice that of A (Hertz (Hz) can be written as cps).

Millihenrys (mH) and microhenrys (μH) are smaller values of henry (H) for inductance.

25. Reactance of coil increases with increased inductance.

A   1 henry   B   2 henry

coil

AC   AC

26. Reactance of coil increases with frequency.

A   1 henry   B   1 henry

50 c/s   100 c/s

Reactance of Capacitor

A capacitor has two closely spaced plates insulated from each other. If we connect an e.m.f., there will be only a brief surge of current as the capacitor charges to the applied voltage. If we remove the e.m.f. and place a wire across the capacitor, current will surge briefly as it loses its charge. Current flows only with a changing e.m.f. (see page 28).

In Figure 27a, AC is connected to the capacitor and a certain current flows. If we make the capacitor larger (27b), the current is larger too, because the reactance is lower. Reactance falls with an increase in capacity or frequency. In Figure 28a we apply 50 c/s AC to the capacitor. At (28b), we apply 100 c/s. The reactance of the capacitor falls with increased frequency.

$$X_c = \frac{1}{2\pi f C}$$

Where:

X_c = Capacitive reactance in ohms
2π = Angular constant
f = Frequency in cycles per second
C = Capacity in farads

Does it Matter?

Figure 29 shows a transformer (see page 40). Primary P takes audio signals from amplifier; secondary S supplies loudspeaker. Capacitor C is across the primary. Higher frequen-

27. Reactance of capacitor falls with increased capacity.

A   1 μF   B   2 μF

AC   AC

28. Reactance of capacitor falls with increased frequency.

A   1 μF   B   1 μF

50 c/s   100 c/s

cies more readily pass through C and do not flow through the primary. This acts as a 'top cut' tone control.

In Figure 30 capacitor C1 is from an audio amplifier tube plate, and by-passes or loses higher frequencies to ground.

The effect is changed by placing part of the variable resistor VR1 in circuit. VR1 is a variable top cut tone control.

29. Falling reactance of capacitor 'cuts' high frequencies.

30. Tone control circuits.

The switch S1 selects a small capacitor C2, a medium value capacitor C3, or a large capacitor C4. C2 lets high frequencies pass easily. C3 lets some lower frequencies pass. C4 allows low frequencies to pass readily. Tone controls are often found in receivers and amplifiers. Most make use of the fact that capacitive reactance falls with increased frequency.

Inductive reactance also has many uses. In Figure 31 a rectifier supplies a power filter. Output from the rectifier

31. Use for inductive reactance.

inductor L

supply   C1   equipment
                                    C2

has pronouned ripple. L is a choke with high inductance. It hinders fluctuations in current. Capacitor C1 acts as a reservoir. The inductor L refuses to let ripples pass, and capacitor C2 provides almost pure direct current. This is called 'smoothing' (see page 45).

In Figure 32a radio frequency (RF) signals and audio frequency (AF) signals arise at collector C. The radio frequency choke hinders RF, so this goes through the small capacitor C1. The choke reactance is low at low frequency, so AF passes through it and is taken off by the larger capacitor C2.

At [32b], a high frequency noise filter choke is placed in an audio circuit. It does not let high frequencies pass, and so reduces surface noise when playing records.

32. Blocking the movement of high frequencies.

X RF

radio frequency choke

C1

RF and AF

C

direct current supply

R1

C2

Y

audio
frequencies

A

B

noise filter

33. Supplying a screen grid

250V+

R1
?

C1
G2
?

150V needed

34. A problem in cathode bias

HT+

5mA

S

25mA

15V needed

R1
?

C1

HT−

A pentode as amplifier is shown in Figure 33. The supply is 250 volts, but the screen grid G2 should have only 150 volts. Since 250–150 = 100, resistor R1 should drop 100 volts.

The current flowing through R1 is measured or found from a tube manual. It is 5mA. Recalling

that $\dfrac{E}{I} = R$, we can say that $\dfrac{100}{0.005} = 20,000$ ohms for R1.

What power is dissipated in R1?

$Watts = E \times I = 100 \times 0.005 = 0.5$ watt. So we use a 20K ½-watt resistor. G2 needs to be grounded at operating frequency. So C1 is a 0.05 μF 250 volt capacitor.

At the output stage of the receiver, 15 volts should be present at the cathode [34]. Cathode current is 25 + 5mA = 30mA or 0.03A.

So R1 is $\dfrac{15}{0.03} = 500$ ohms.

For audio frequencies and 15 volts, C1 can be 25 μF 25 working volts.

A test instrument for two voltage ranges—0 to 10 volts and 0 to 100 volts—is shown in Figure 35. For a full-scale reading, 1mA must flow (.001A). This is to show 10 volts with R1. R1 $= \dfrac{10}{0.001} = 10,000$ ohms. Similarly, R2 = 100,000 ohms.

35. Resistor values for a voltmeter

36. DC working conditions of a transistor amplifier.

A transistor circuit where we suspect the transistor is not drawing the correct collector current, though all resistors and the supply voltage are correct, is shown in Figure 36. The collector current should be 2mA. The simplest test is to measure the voltage across the resistor, from X to Y. From $E = I \times R$, the voltage should be $0.002 \times 1,000 = 2$ volts.

A meter reads only 0.5 volt.

$$\text{From} \quad I = \frac{E}{R} = \frac{0.5}{1,000}$$

we see that the transistor collector current is actually 0.5mA.

Electronic Circuit Diagrams

For some electronic equipment, components could be shown in outline, with connections, in a scale drawing just as in the apparatus.

But it is usually better to have a circuit diagram where simple symbols represent various components. Symbols are often simplified representations of the components. By comparing components and their symbols, you will become familiar with them.

Lines represent wires. These may be joined as in Figure 37a. They may cross without contact [37b]. Dots [37c] show connecting points such as sockets, which could be for plugs connected to a loudspeaker, or could be used for some other purpose.

A fixed resistor symbol is shown in Figure 38, together with three resistors in a small part of a circuit. In Figures 39a and 39b is shown a variable resistor. If connections are taken to X and Y, moving the sliding contact (arrow) to the right increases the resistance actually in circuit.

The resistance element may be wire for low values, but carbon is used for high values. The track can be in a semicircle, and rotating a spindle moves the contact along the track [39c]. Figure 39d is a typical component.

B, C and D are potentiometers. If a potential—such as an audio signal voltage—is taken to X and Z, any required level can be tapped off by moving slider Y. This happens with an audio volume control.

Switches

In Figure 40 is shown an on/off switch. It could be a supply voltage toggle switch, low voltage rotary switch, or any other component.

A volume control often has a switch. It can be a single on/off type (single pole), or it can be two on/off switches (double pole) which work together to interrupt two circuits.

The rotary switch in Figure 40 has a contact X, which can transfer a circuit to 1, 2 or 3, the switch having three positions. It is '1-pole 3-way'. It could have more contacts and more ways, as required.

37. How connections are shown.

38. Resistors

B

C

39. Variable resistors and potentiometers

A

X   Z
B
Y

X Y Z

C

Y   Z

X   D

40. How switches are shown

2   3
1
X

2   3
1
X

25

Inductors and Coils

Insulated wire wound upon an insulated tube forms a coil or inductor [41]. We can increase the inductance by using more turns, or having a larger coil. Or we can place a core in the winding to concentrate the magnetic field and raise its inductance.

The inductor might be of very small inductance and have few turns [42a]. Larger inductance coils have more turns [42b]. The coil could have a tapped winding—or two or more windings on the same insulated tube [42c]. If there are very many turns they may be in sections [42d]. This is a 'high frequency choke'—an inductor which prevents the passage of high frequencies.

Special materials have to be used for cores for radio frequency coils (those that work at radio frequencies). A core of ferrite or iron dust material placed in the coil winding intensifies the magnetic field and raises the inductance, so if we want to adjust the inductance, we can use a threaded

41. Radio frequency (RF) chokes

42. Other small inductors

A.

B.

C.

D.

core, and screw it in or out [43]. In the symbol, the dotted line is the core, and the sloping line shows it is adjustable. To simplify large circuit diagrams, cores are often not shown.

LF Cores

At low frequencies, cores can be made from various alloys [44]. Thin sheet iron was once used.

The winding is often on a bobbin, entirely surrounded by the core. One limb fits inside the winding. This core is often of thin metal 'stampings' or laminations, and enough are used to make up the thickness wanted.

Since this inductor prevents the ready flow of low frequencies it is a 'low frequency choke'. Such a choke is often employed to help remove ripple in a supply from a power circuit, and is then called a 'smoothing choke'. In order to be used for this purpose, it would normally have an inductance of several henrys.

43. Adjustable core allows inductance to be changed.

44. Audio chokes with core made from laminations.

Capacitors

Two metal plates near each other but not in contact form a capacitor and can store a charge [45]. If we connect a voltage to X-X a deficiency of electrons arises at one plate, and a surplus at the other. Electrostatic stress arises in the insulating space between plates. The capacitor is 'charged' with a power depending on 'capacity' or charge-storing ability. Unit of capacitance = farad (F).

If X-X are joined together, the capacitor gives up its charge. We can increase the capacity to hold a charge by placing the plates nearer each other, and in other ways. The insulation between plates is the 'dielectric'. Capacitors are made with mica and ceramic insulation, or foil rolled up with insulating paper and in a tube [46]. Or metallic conductors may be deposited on an insulator.

'Electrolytic' capacitors are so made that an applied voltage must be of the correct polarity. These capacitors are of some set value and are called 'fixed capacitors'.

We may need to change the capacitance at any time and

45. A fixed capacitor

X   X

X   X —electrostatic field

46. Some capacitors for electronic equipment

disc

1000 PF

molded mica

0·01 μF

0·5 μF 350v

paper tubular

+

+

28

8 μF 450 v

electrolytic

47. Variable capacitor

48. 2-gang and trimmer capacitors

moving plate

fixed plate

2-gang

trimmers

for this we want a 'variable capacitor'. A small variable capacitor can have one fixed plate, and one moving plate attached to a spindle [47]. Rotating the spindle changes the extent to which moving and fixed plates overlap each other, and thus alters the capacity. Capacitance is least with the plates not overlapping at all.

We may wish to tune two circuits simultaneously in a radio receiver and can then use a 2-gang capacitor [48]. By having many fixed and many moving plates, the total capacity of each section can be increased. Sometimes the capacity has to be adjusted when first putting a circuit into proper working condition. A 'trimmer' is then used. It is adjusted with a screwdriver or other tool, and brings moving and fixed plates closer to increase the capacitance.

A Voltage Amplifier

The circuit in Figure 49 is the first audio amplifier stage of a receiver or large audio amplifier. It increases the voltage of audio signals obtained from a pick-up employed to play records, or from a receiver detector.

Capacitor C1 isolates earlier direct current circuits from the base B of the transistor, supplied by the resistors R1 and R2. Resistor R3 applies a small negative bias to the emitter E. Bias increases when emitter current rises. This helps to make working conditions stable. C2 grounds the emitter E at audio frequencies.

Current from collector C flows through resistor R4. Amplified signal voltages are developed across R4. Signals are taken off by capacitor C3.

A practical layout of Figure 49 is shown in Figure 50a. Figure 50b is the same amplifier assembled in more compact form.

49. One-stage transistor amplifier

50. Practical assembly of Figure 49

A.

B.

Block Diagrams

We may show the essential parts of a circuit without going into detail. Block diagrams do this. Figure 51 is a block diagram of a large amplifier. Each 'box' represents one section — Section 1 is an audio frequency amplifier like Figure 49. So is Section 2. Section 3 is an output stage, or amplifier which supplies appreciable power. Signals reach it from Section 2, and its output goes to the loudspeaker.

Figure 52a is for playing stereo records. The stereo pick-up produces left-hand and right-hand channel signals. These go to the balancing section, where the relative volume is adjusted. Amplifiers supply outputs for right-hand and left-hand speakers.

Figure 52b is a block diagram showing a photoelectric counter. An item interrupts light falling on the cell, causing electrical output to work a counter.

51. Block diagram of audio amplifier

52. Block diagrams of stereo amplifier and photo-electric counter

53. Transistor symbols and vacuum triode

Other Symbols

The symbol for a PNP transistor is shown in Figure 53a; that for the NPN transistor at 53b. Figure 53c is the symbol for a triode tube. The tube might be of any type.

Remember, most symbols are simplified representations of the component or its function! The relay [54] illustrates this. Tags X-X take current to an electromagnet winding. The spring-actuated contact Y normally rests against the fixed contact 1. When current flows in the winding, the armature Y moves and switches the circuit to 2.

Sometimes items in a circuit can be omitted, to obtain a diagram which is easier to follow, or to ignore repeated details. In Figure 55 the switch allows inductor L1, L2, L3 or L4 to be selected. This is shown in full at [55a]. At [55b]

54. Relay

55. Omissions for clarity

the actual way in which inductor L1 is connected is shown and inductors L2, L3, and L4 are omitted.

Simplifications of this kind are very useful when there are several switch positions and sections, and possibly quite a large number of inductors or other parts.

Theoretical circuits do not usually take into account the actual way in which the equipment is assembled. For example, an amplifier circuit could be assembled on a panel and occupy quite a large space. Or it could be arranged on a smaller panel, with components close together, or made with miniature components to the smallest possible size. But in all these cases it might be the same circuit.

Various other symbols are shown in Figure 56.

56. Various other symbols

Magnetism is Important

An unmagnetized bar has all its particles at random [57a]. Magnetizing it draws them into similar polarity [57b]. The bar magnet [57c] has a north pole at one end, and south pole at the other end. Other shapes are the horses shoe [57d] and ring magnets [57e].

If the north pole of one magnet is near the south pole of another magnet, an attractive force arises. But if a north pole is placed by a north pole, or a south pole by a south pole, a repulsive force pushes the magnets apart. Both poles attract ferrous or iron objects.

Various specially shaped magnet assemblies are used [58]. That at Figure 58a has curved ends to accommodate the rotating coil of a meter; [58b] is for a similar purpose. Figure 58c is for a moving-coil speaker or microphone.

If we connect a coil to a battery or other direct current supply, a magnetic field is created [59a]. It has north and south poles, and exists so long as current flows. The mag-

57. Permanent magnets

A.

B.

C. N   S

D.

N   S

E.

58. Shaped magnets for electronic apparatus

A.

B.

⌐ pole pieces ⌐

gap

C.

34

netic field arises when the switch is closed and current begins [59b]. When the switch is opened, the field collapses [59c]. This generates an electromotive force or e.m.f. in the coil, of opposite polarity to that from the battery. If the supply polarity is reversed, the magnetic poles are also reversed. If we connect the coil to an alternating current supply [60] current flows back and forth through the coil. At each reversal of direction, the magnetic field collapses and arises with opposite polarity. Most electro-magnets have cores allowing concentration of magnetic force. Current in a winding creates a magnetic field.

The reverse arises. If a magnet is moved in or out of a coil, an e.m.f. is produced [61]. Relative motion must exist between the field and conductor. The magnetic field can be from a permanent magnet, or from another electromagnet. These effects are used in generators and other devices where the rapid motion of magnetic fields produces strong currents.

59. Field surrounding an inductor

battery

closed

B.

open

C.

——lines of
magnetic force——

S

60. Inductor supplied from alternating current and with core

AC input

field changes
polarity each
half-cycle

field changes polarity each half-cycle

—— core ——

35

Moving-Coil Meter—The D'Arsonval Movement
In Figure 62, a strong field exists in the circular space between the shaped pole pieces. A coil is pivoted to rotate in this gap. Current is fed to it by hairsprings, and a pointer is attached.

When current flows in the coil, the magnetic field surrounding the conductors interacts with the permanent magnet field, and the coil rotates slightly. This can show current, voltage, or other things we wish to know. When current ceases, the coil returns to its original position.

61. Changing magnetic field generates e.m.f.

62. Moving-coil meter

Moving-Coil Speaker
This embodies a cone carrying a very light coil, which receives current by flexible leads [63]. The coil occupies a narrow gap in a magnet assembly, and can move in and out in line with the cone axis.

Audio signals taken to the coil generate a fluctuating magnetic field. Interaction between this field and the fixed

63. Moving-coil loudspeaker

cone

speech coil

flexible pigtails

magnet field causes the coil and cone to move in and out. This is transmitted to the air, producing sound waves.

The winding is often called the 'speech coil'. 'Permanent magnet' moving-coil speakers have a permanent magnet assembly. 'Energized' speakers have an electromagnet, or winding, on the center limb of the assembly, and current in this produces the magnetic field.

In a moving-coil microphone, vibrations of the cone and coil produce an e.m.f. in the coil.

'OR' Gate

Small cores are used for various purposes in computers. In Figure 64 an input at A OR at B will give an output. This is called 'OR' gate.

64. Magnetic 'OR' gate for computer

input A

output

input B

winding

⌐ core

laminated core
for A.C. solenoid⌐

65. Solenoids

Solenoid and Magnetic Field

When current flows in a winding, a core becomes magnetized. If the core is out of the winding, magnetic forces pull it in [65]. The limbs of the plunger and the fixed portion of the assembly can be shaped to assist this action by concentrating the magnetic field. A solenoid may control fuel or liquid flow valves, mechanical step-by-step counters, and many other devices.

Sometimes we wish to avoid magnetic fields, as in 'non-inductive' wire-wound resistors. Then we try to make one part of the field cancel another part [66]. Here, A is a wire-wound resistor, resembling an electromagnet. B has a loop: current reverses and flows back. C uses thin flat mica. One-half of each turn lies flat under the other half. D reverses the winding direction half-way.

Electrons are influenced by the presence of magnetic

66. Non-inductive wire-wound resistors

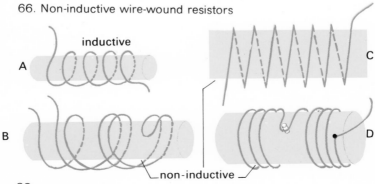

inductive

A

B

C

D

non-inductive

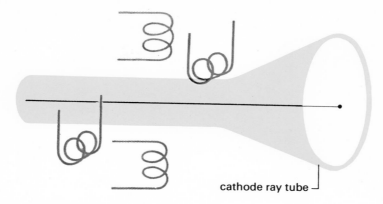

cathode ray tube

67. Magnetic deflection of cathode ray

fields. This is useful with television picture tubes, and with magnetrons, and so on.

A stream of electrons is emitted by the electron gun of a cathode ray tube [67]. The beam passes between coils on the tube. When no current flows in these coils, the beam travels straight to the screen, and produces a central bright spot on the face of the tube.

Current flowing in the coils produces a field which curves the electron path up or down, or from side to side. In this way the beam is made to strike the screen at any point we want.

By altering the strength and polarity of current in the coils, the beam can be made to travel over any part of the picture-tube face. The coils are specially shaped to lie around the tube [68]. Electromagnetic deflection of the electron beam is used in television receivers.

68. Arrangement of coils on cathode-ray tube

P   S

69. An air-cored transformer

70. Transformer with core

P   S

core

P   S

primary ⌐   ⌐ secondary

Transformers

Transformers are useful devices relying on electromagnetic effects. They have two windings [69]. The primary (P) receives power from some source (an antenna, amplifier, or alternating current supply). The secondary (S) delivers power to a following device or circuit (a transistor or tube, a loudspeaker, a motor, an electric lamp, etc.).

The transformer may be 'air cored' for high frequencies [69]—that is, it may have no solid core material. Currents in the primary develop a fluctuating electromagnetic field, rising and falling rapidly according to the current. This field cuts the turns of the secondary, and induces an e.m.f. in the winding.

For lower frequencies, audio circuits, or alternating current supply solid cores are placed in the windings. These concentrate the magnetic field, and are generally made up from thin laminations. (See also page 27).

Primary and secondary may be on separate limbs of the core [70] or a bobbin fitted on the center limb.

The transformer changes or transforms one voltage

to another, according to the 'turns ratio', or relationship between primary turns and secondary turns [71], given by: Transformer formulas:

$$\frac{Np}{Ns}=\frac{ep}{es}=\frac{is}{ip}=\frac{Zp}{Zs}$$

The subscripts denote primary and secondary where:

N = Number of turns
e = Voltage
i = Current
Z = Impedance

71. Turns ratio of transformers

1:1   3:1

1:2

These relationships presuppose 100% transformer efficiency. Suppose the secondary has one-third the number of primary turns. The ratio is 3:1. If the primary received 240 volts AC, the secondary would deliver 80 volts. But if the secondary had twice as many turns as the primary, the ratio would be 1:2. If the primary received 240 volts, the secondary would receive 480 volts.

Transformers produce the voltages we want, or couple circuits together. A transformer may have several windings [72]. The primary here is tapped for 210/230/250 volt. One secondary supplies 5 volts, another 6.3 volts, and a third 500 volts center tapped, or 250/0/250 volts. That is, 250 volts each side of the tapping.

72. Typical supply transformer

250V
230V
210V

5V
250V
0V
250V

laminations forming core

6.3V

0

leads colored for identification

73. A magnetron

plates

coil

cathode

74. An 8-cavity 10cm. magnetron

machined block

cavity resonant circuits

straps

cathode

output

The Magnetron

A small 2-anode magnetron—a device which can produce radio frequency energy—is shown in Figure 73. If no magnetic field were present, negative electrons would flow from cathode to positive plates. When the magnetic field intensity is raised the electrons take curved paths and tend to circle the cathode.

An alternating potential is obtained on the anodes from a resonant circuit. Electrons approaching the higher potential accelerate. Those approaching the lower potential lose velocity, so that clusters of electrons tend to revolve around the cathode, maintaining the oscillation.

Operation is in brief duty periods (less than one per cent) with high power at high frequency. Large radar magnetrons deliver many thousands of watts, at centimeter wave lengths. For very high frequencies, the plates are formed with cavities which act as the resonant circuit. Anodes and cavities are arranged in a ring [74].

Cyclotron

The cyclotron [75] can supply high-energy particles and has two D-shaped members. They are supplied with high frequency alternating current at many kilovolts. The whole is in a vacuum and placed between magnetic poles. Particles travel in a curved path because of the magnetic field. Particles approach each of the D-shaped members as the potential is rising, and this accelerates them. They travel around and around, gaining velocity until ejected through the opening. They bombard other particles, and facts are learned about the nucleus. The synchrotron, with magnets around a circular track, has accelerated particles up to nearly the speed of light. Particles generated include protons, deuterons and alpha particles.

Magnetohydrodynamics, or Gas Flow Electricity

If a conductor is moved across the lines of force of a magnetic field, an electromotive force is generated [76]. When a flow of ionized gas is directed between the poles of a magnet, an e.m.f. is also produced. Current can be taken away by conducting plates.

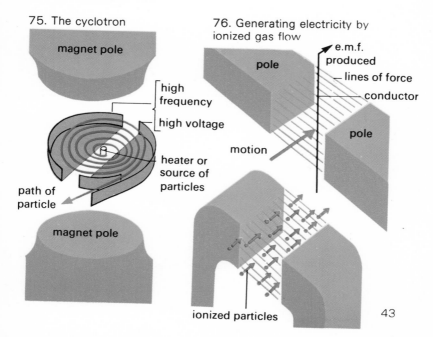

75. The cyclotron

magnet pole

high frequency

high voltage

heater or source of particles

path of particle

magnet pole

76. Generating electricity by ionized gas flow

pole

e.m.f. produced

lines of force

conductor

pole

motion

ionized particles

43

Electron Tubes

A directly heated filament is a thin wire heated by an electric current. It then emits electrons.

Often we have the surface which emits electrons separated

77. Directly heated filament and indirectly heated cathode

electrically from the filament [77]. The filament is electrically insulated from the tube or cathode, which reaches working temperature after an interval. The filament is the heater; the tubes are 'indirectly heated'.

Diode

A thermionic diode has two essential electrodes, and it lets current pass one way only. The diode has a metal plate by the cathode [78]. In working circuits we assume that current will be applied to the heater: so these connections are often omitted in diagrams.

If the plate has a positive potential, electrons emitted by the cathode flow to the plate. If the plate is negative, electrons emitted by the cathode are not attracted. No current flows. The diode allows electrons to flow from cathode to plate, but not from plate to cathode.

78. Thermionic diode

79. Diode as AC power rectifier

input

output

alternating

Diode Rectifier

Direct current flows steadily in one direction. Alternating current flows first one way, then the other. With 60 cycle per second supplies there are 60 cycles each second [79]. If we apply this to a diode, current passes only during those intervals when the diode plate is positive. Half-cycles of opposite polarity are suppressed, so we obtain pulsating direct current.

A single diode has cathode and plate. This is also a 'half-wave rectifier'. A 'full-wave rectifier' [80] has two plates, and can be connected to make use of both half-waves of the AC supply cycles.

80. A full-wave rectifier

cathode

plate 1

plate 2

mica supports

pins

Diode Current

Suppose we provide any chosen voltage by moving the slider of a potentiometer VR [81]. A milliammeter indicates the diode current. As the voltage increases, more electrons are attracted to the plate, and current rises. When practically all the electrons are attracted, the current levels off, and scarcely increases at all, even with a much higher plate voltage. This is the maximum, or saturation current.

Full-Wave Rectification

A single diode in a half-wave rectification circuit allowed half-cycles of an alternating supply to flow, so we obtained pulsating direct current. Full-wave rectification is possible with two plates or two separate single diodes [82]. The transformer secondary is center-tapped. For one half-cycle one diode is positive, and for the other half-cycle the other diode is positive. So both half-cycles are utilized.

81. Current flowing through a diode

82. Full-wave rectification

Much AC equipment has a rectifier which supplies direct current for other tubes. The pulsating DC has to be made steady and continuous. 'Smoothing capacitors' across the supply, and a 'smoothing choke' in series do this [83]. The capacitors store energy and give out current. The choke opposes changes in current. Thus a smooth supply, almost like that from a battery, is available. Plate voltages are called the 'B' supply.

Uses for Diodes

Thermionic diode power rectifiers [84] can supply large currents at high voltage. Smaller diodes provide detection or demodulation, or rectify signals for automatic volume control bias. With an indirectly heated cathode, heater and cathode can be connected to different circuits. But if it has a directly heated cathode or filament, there is no separate cathode connection. This can be important with power rectifiers.

83. Power supply smoothing circuit

— choke —

84. Thermionic rectifiers with directly heated and indirectly heated cathodes

— plates

cathode —

heater

heater

The Triode

A diode has two important electrodes: cathode and plate. The triode has a third electrode, a grid of thin wires, between cathode and plate [85]. Electrons emitted from cathode to plate pass between the meshes of the grid. The triode can 'amplify' signals, or increase their strength. If the grid is at or near zero potential it has little effect on the flow of electrons.

Suppose a meter placed between the plate and supply shows 8mA with −1 volt [86]. If we make the grid more negative, electrons are repelled from its vicinity, so that

85. A triode has control grid between cathode and plate

plate — grid —

plate current is reduced. With −2 volts at the grid, plate current has fallen to about 6mA. At −3 volts current is 4mA. If the grid is made very negative, virtually all the electrons emitted by the cathode are repelled by the negative charge on it, and do not reach the plate.

Changes in grid voltage cause changes in plate current. This gird is called the 'control grid'. A steady D-C voltage is called 'grid bias'. Changing the grid potential by 1 volt causes plate current to change by 2mA. The tube has a mutual conductance of 2mA per volt, or 2mA/V.

86. Plate current controlled by grid voltage

We can apply various voltages, and read current with a meter [87]. As we raise the voltage, current increases. At 50 volts it is 4mA, but it has risen to 6mA at 100 volts. If the bias voltage is unchanged, altering the anode potential by 50 volts changes the anode current by 2mA [88]. In Figure 86 changing the grid potential by 1 volt changed the anode current by 2mA. So altering grid potential by 1 volt has the same result on anode current as changing the anode potential by 50 volts.

87. Changing plate voltage also changes plate current

88. Plate voltage and current

plate

49

Triode Amplifier

An audio signal is applied to X in Figure 89. Resistor R1 completes the tube grid circuit. Cathode current flows through R2. We need the control grid to be—2 volts relative to the cathode K. So R2 drops 2 volts. C1 by-passes R2 at frequencies to be amplified.

With no signal at X, bias is—2 volts and plate current is 6mA. The audio signal is 2 volts from peak to peak, so swings the grid from 1 volt to 3 volts. Plate current swings from 8mA to 4mA. The voltage dropped in resistor R3 depends on plate current. So the plate voltage also swings up and down. An amplified signal is taken off by capacitor C2. Such capacitors isolate other circuits [90].

More Electrodes

A screen grid G2 betweeen control grid G1 and plate [91] has a positive potential. Plate current depends less on the

89. Thermionic triode amplifier

90. Isolating direct current circuits by coupling capacitors

plate voltage, and amplification is increased. Electrons may be knocked off the plate and return to the positively charged screen grid. The suppressor grid G3 hinders this. This tube is a pentode. Shaped plates between screen grid and plate in a 'beam tetrode' also hinder the flow of electrons from anode to screen grid.

We control the electron stream from two circuits by using a tube with more grids, such as a heptode [92]. Signals applied to grids G1 and G3 control the electron flow. Grids 2 and 4 form a screen each side of G3. G5 is the suppressor grid.

A duo-triode has two triodes in a single bulb. A duo-diode triode has two diodes together with a triode assembly. In the same way, there are other tubes, such as triode-hexodes, triode pentodes, pentodes with diodes, and duo-pentodes.

91 Screen grid, tetrode and pentode valves

shaped plate
beam plates
G1
G2
glass bulb
supports in glass base
beam tetrode
pins
locating pin

screen grid
plate
suppressor grid
G2
G1
A
cathode
control grid
G3
G2
G1
B

pentode
C

beam tetrode
D

92 Two more multi-electrode valves

converter
G2
G4
G3
G1
G5
K.G5

duo-triode
A1
A2
G1
G2
K1
K2

51

Variable-Mu Pentodes or Remote Cut-off Pentodes

Amplification can be controlled by using a grid having irregular spacing [93]. By increasing the negative bias, the amplification can be reduced to a very small fraction. The tube might have a mutual conductance of 5mA/V with zero bias, falling to 0.005mA/V and 20 volt bias.

Negative Resistance Condition

If a screen grid tube has certain screen grid and plate potentials, electrons strike the plate at a velocity causing other

93. Control grid of variable mu tube

electrons to be liberated. This 'secondary emission' electrons return to the screen grid. When potentials are suitable, and the screen grid potential is higher than the plate, secondary emission is considerable. If the plate voltage is increased, electrons strike it with added velocity, and liberate more secondary electrons. So over a certain part of the operating curve plate current *falls* for an increase in plate voltage [94]. This is 'negative resistance'. It can cancel the actual or positive resistance of a circuit, sustaining oscillation.

Tube Component Parts

Figure 95 shows parts of a small transmitting tube. Many receiver tubes are quite similar in design, though generally

94 Negative resistance screen grid valve

95. A small transmitting tube—component parts

with all connections to base pins. The heater is in the cathode. Then come control grid, screen grid, beam forming plates and plate. The whole is supported by mica parts pushed inside a glass bulb. As high voltages are present, the plate has a cap. The insulated base has pins. Smaller tubes may be all glass, with pins in a glass base.

Gas-Filled Thyratron
This contains a gas which ionizes when sufficient current flows, reducing the internal resistance [96]. When the grid is sufficiently negative no electron current flows. Less negative potential causes electrons to flow, ionizing the gas. The tube conducts heavily until the plate potential is reduced.

Semiconductors

The electrons of an atom have various energy levels so that they can be thought of as occupying different bands or positions. Free electrons in the outer position, or shell, can move from atom to atom, forming an electric current.

Germanium has 32 electrons, with four in the outer shell. By adding impurities, an excess or lack of electrons is arranged. Indium has 49 electrons, with three in the outer shell. This is one less than the germanium outer shell, so an electron from a germanium atom can move in to occupy the space, leaving a germanium atom with a deficiency of one electron. This, a positive 'hole', can accept an electron from another germanium atom [97].

Antimony has 51 electrons, with five in the outer shell. This extra electron can displace an adjoining electron, which in turn can move elsewhere.

Lack of an electron leaves a positive charge, so the crystal is termed 'P-type'. Excess of electrons constitutes a negative charge and gives 'N-type' material. Movement of the electrons or hole carriers forms an electric current.

A semiconductor junction diode is a junction of N-type and P-type regions, and is often called a PN diode. Current in N-type germanium is conveyed mostly by electrons, but in the P-type mostly by holes [98].

The diode allows current to pass readily in the 'forward' direction. There are many positive holes to move across to the N-region, and numerous negative electrons to travel to the P-region [99]. This represents a large flow of current

97 Germanium with positive and negative carriers

Outer electrons

P-Type

hole

electron

indium

N-type

antimony

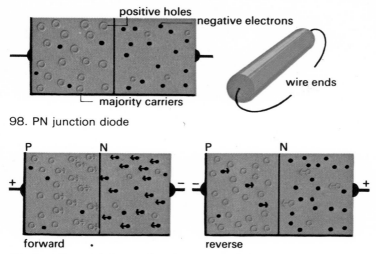

positive holes negative electrons

majority carriers

wire ends

98. PN junction diode

P   N   P   N

forward   reverse

99. Junction with forward and reverse voltage

across the junction. With the voltage reversed, there are few negative electrons in the P-region, and few positive holes in the N-region, so that the current is small. Semiconductor diodes are made to suit the voltage, current and frequency [100]. Point contact diodes pass small currents, but can operate at very high frequencies.

Germanium rectifiers tend to fail around 75° C, while silicon can withstand up to about 200° C. Thus a silicon rectifier is less affected by rises in temperature, and can operate with currents of many amperes.

100. Some semiconductor diodes

glass encased point contact

general-purpose

silicon power rectifier

Semiconductor diodes are now much used in power supply circuits for rectification. They are small in size, have low forward resistance, can handle high voltages and current, and need no separate heater supply.

Many electronic circuits, including those of receivers and amplifiers, require direct current. The alternating current supply is usually taken to the primary (P) of a power transformer [101]. This isolates equipment from any actual connection with the supply. Voltage can be reduced or increased by a suitable turns ratio.

The diode allows current to pass readily one way and so can charge a reservoir capacitor. Compare this with the half-wave tube circuit. Semiconductor diodes can also be used in full-wave circuits, to make use of both half-cycles of the AC supply, as with tubes.

When rectifiers are working at maximum current, heat is produced. This is carried away by a metal plate or heat sink. Rectifiers may be connected in series or parallel, to obtain a higher voltage or current rating, or they can be stacked in special assemblies [102].

101. Power diode allows DC to be obtained from AC

102. Rectifier stack with convection cooling

Compensating Diode

In transistor receivers and amplifiers, working conditions of the output transistors which supply the loudspeaker are quite critical. Wrong bias will increase battery drain, or cause distortion.

Base bias which is suitable for a new battery may be unsatisfactory with one that is partly discharged. The temperature at which they are operating affects somewhat the working of transistors.

A compensating diode [103] helps overcome this. The diode's resistance (and transistor operation) varies with the temperature. When battery voltage falls, current through the diode is less. Its resistance rises, helping to shift the base supply more negative and restore satisfactory working.

RF Probe

The point contact diode has extremely small internal capacity, and can operate at very high frequencies. It is suitable for a radio frequency probe [104]. The probe can be taken to any circuit point where RF is present.

103. Diode to stabilize performance

compensating diode

104. Isolated VHF probe

point contact diode

capacitor

57

Base 1·5mm in diameter and 0·1 mm thick — wires

N-type material

collector

base

emitter

C

B

E

E B C

105. A PNP transistor

emitter

base

thin diffusion layer

106. A planar transistor   collector

Transistors

A transistor has a central region, or base, of one kind of semiconductor material, with junctions of an opposite kind of material on each side. A PNP transistor has positive-negative-positive material, with a negative central base [105]. The NPN transistor has negative-positive-negative material—a positive central region or base.

For the PNP transistor, pellets of indium are fused on by heating, and diffuse into the base to form P-type regions. The whole is fitted with leads and sealed in a protective case.

Such a transistor becomes less efficient at high frequencies. An alloy junction transistor has a base region only a small fraction of a millimeter wide. Planar transistors [106] made by alloy diffusion have an extremely thin active base region, and construction which reduces the time required

reverse bias

collector

P

base

N

forward bias

P

+ emitter

107. Large flow of current

large current

Ic

Ib

−

+

collector

P

base

N

P

108. Small flow of current

emitter

small current

Ic

Ib

−

+

for the movement of the current carriers.

The PNP emitter is connected to a positive supply, and the collector to a negative [107]. If the base is appreciably negative, relative to the emitter, the emitter-base junction acts as a diode junction with forward bias. Holes pass into the base, and are drawn by the negative charge of the collector, so that they usually flow to the collector. Current passing through the transistor is large.

If the forward bias is reduced, fewer holes travel to the collector. The current flow is quite small [108]. In a PNP transistor, there is a small movement of 'minority' or negative electron carriers, the 'majority' or most numerous carriers being positive holes—a positive charge equal to an electron. Base and collector currents added together form approximately the emitter current. Almost all the emitter current passes to the collector.

59

Note the important difference between PNP and NPN transistors [109]. The PNP transistor base is negative type material, and majority current carriers are positive holes, caused by a deficiency of negative electrons. Emitter goes to *positive*. With the NPN transistor, the base is positive type material, and electrons are majority carriers. Emitter goes to *negative*.

Note that the arrow symbol is always the emitter, and agrees with the motion of positive hole carriers. We can regard this as the conventional electrical current flow from positive to negative, encountered in some text books. The flow of electron current is from negative to positive. A heavy current may flow if a supply is connected in the wrong polarity to a transistor. If resistors and so on do not impede this current, transistor junction may be damaged.

Internal Feedback
The electrodes of a transistor are very close together and this and other effects cause unwanted feedback from the

109. PNP transistor and NPN transistor compared

110. Screened transistor

base
emitter
screen

collector

collector. In Figure 110, an imaginary capacitor connection from collector to base stands for the unwanted feedback. This is usually unimportant at low frequencies, but troublesome at high frequencies, where special precautions have to be taken to avoid oscillation or other effects.

Transistors for high frequencies may have a fourth lead, or shield, between base and collector [110]. It helps to reduce unwanted feedback.

Receiver transistors [11] are usually quite small, with insulated or metal cases.

They are made for radio frequency amplification, audio amplification, etc. They are also produced in small sizes for miniature equipment.

Power transistors [112] for RF and audio amplification are larger; usually they can be clamped to a metal plate or heat sink, to help avoid overheating. Some transistors are made in similar or matched pairs, in a single case. Other transistors are intended for computer 'logic' and various special applications.

111. Small receiver and amplifier transistors

flat capsule

miniature

RF and audio

112. Power and matched pair transistors

AF power

matched pair

RF power

61

Some Circuit Points

We use transistors in various ways. Some are shown in Figure 113. Here A has input to emitter and base, with output from collector and base. R is a load resistor across which power is developed, or a tuning coil or other device. Both input and output circuits use the base, so A is a *common and grounded base* arrangement.

B has input between base and emitter, and output developed across collector and emitter circuits. It is a *common and grounded emitter*. In the same way C is a *common emitter grounded collector* arrangement.

A, B and C are NPN transistors. D is a PNP transistor with input to base and emitter, and output developed across collector and emitter circuits. It is a *common emitter grounded emitter* circuit.

Some methods provide best power gain. Others operate better at high frequency. Some have high impedance input and low impedance output, or the reverse. The 'impedance' is the 'resistance' at operating frequency. Figure 114 shows the transistor as a current generator, with input impedance R1 and output impedance R2. Maximum useful power results when input and output circuits match R1 and R2.

Dynamic Operation

Figure 115 is a PNP common emitter amplifier, with base bias set by R1 and R2 and output developed across R3. C1 and C2 isolate the stage from other direct current points. R4 provides emitter bias to stabilize operation, and has a by-pass capacitor, C3.

Base current Ib is at some small steady value. Collector current Ic is also at a steady value, and emitter current Ie approximately equals Ib plus Ic. Currents are indicated without regard to polarity. When a signal to be amplified arrives through C1, base current swings up and down with each cycle, as shown in [116-Ib]. Slight increases in base current cause large increases in emitter-collector current. So collector current Ic swings up and down in value, developing an output voltage across R3.

A moving-coil meter would show the average currents [115], an oscilloscope dynamic conditions.

A

B

C

D

113. Ways of using a transistor

114. Impedance matching

115. Static conditions of transistor

R1

R3

Ic

C2

C1

Ib

R2

Ie

R4

C3

0

0

0

116. Dynamic working during amplification

Ib

0

Ie

0

$Ie=Ic+Ib$

AUDIO, RADIO, TELEVISION, TAPES

Audio Amplifiers

A signal is 'amplified' to make it stronger. An audio amplifier deals with frequencies from about 15 c/s to 15,000 c/s. Musical items mostly lie in the 50 c/s to 2,000 c/s range, but 'harmonics' must be reproduced for good results. The electrical output of a record-player pick-up may be a few millivolts. A loudspeaker needs much more power, so signals are amplified [117].

Figure 118 is a triode tube audio amplifier. There is 2 volts negative bias through R1 for the control grid. The tube passes 1mA from its cathode to its plate. Plate current flows through R2. From Ohm's Law $(E = I \times R)$ the voltage dropped at R2 is 100 volts. Suppose a positive

117. Audio spectrum and need for amplification

signal peak of 1 volt reaches the grid [119a]. The grid voltage is now —1 volt. Plate current rises to 1.5mA. So 1.5mA flows through R2. The voltage drop is now 150 volts, leaving 50 volts at the plate. Imagine that a 1 volt negative peak reaches the grid, B. This adds to the —2 volts present, giving —3 volts. Suppose plate current falls to 0.5mA. The voltage lost in R2 is now 50 volts, so the plate potential is 200–50 = 150 volts.

Hence by applying a signal which swings 1 volt above and below zero we have obtained an output or plate voltage which swings from 150 volts to 50 volts.

C1 is the usual coupling capacitor [120]. It interrupts any direct current path, but it has little reactance at audio frequency, and therefore lets signals pass. In the same way, C2 feeds another stage.

118. A triode tube audio amplifier

200V+

R2
100K

C1

1mA
100V

out

R1

in

−
2V
+

1mA

HT−

119. The triode amplifying a signal

200V+

R2

2V peak-to-peak

+

A

−1V

R1

−2

200V+

R2

B

−3V

120. Coupling capacitors block
of DC

+

C2

out

in

C1

−

65

We need the control grid to receive a small negative bias voltage. Figure 121 has cathode bias resistor R3, which must drop 2 volts with 1mA passing. $\dfrac{E}{I} = R$. So R3 is 2,000 ohms.

C3 across R3 'by-passes' the cathode to ground at operating frequency. We often use a pentode and get higher 'gain' or amplification than from a triode [122]. VR is a potentiometer which allows any portion of the signal voltage to be taken, and so acts as volume control. RS supplies the screen grid G2, and CS is the screen grid by-pass capacitor. The suppressor grid is at the same potential as the cathode.

121 Current through R3 develops bias

122 Volume control with pentode

Useful work is done by the plate load resistor R2—a signal voltage is developed across it. The tube, with resistors and other components, is termed a 'stage'. The 'stage gain' or amplification achieved is less than the amplification factor of the tube.

Imaginary resistor Ra [123a] represents the tube internal impedance and the plate load resistor R2 is chosen to suit this. With output tubes this is termed the 'optimum' (best) load. In Figure 123b it is furnished by the transformer and speaker. By choosing a suitable transformer ratio, we can provide any optimum load we choose.

Loudspeaker impedance will often be about 2 to 15 ohms. Transformer ratio is usually from about 15:1 to 60:1.

123 Valve anode load

R2

speaker

ra

A

B

124 Three-stage amplifier

pick-up

A B C

speaker

Cascaded Stages

We usually need more amplification than is provided by one stage, so use two or more stages [124]. Here A could be an initial voltage amplifier [122], B a further amplifier stage [121], and C an output stage working a loudspeaker.

Transformer Coupling

In Figure 125 the transformer primary winding receives audio signals from an earlier stage. The secondary delivers signals to the next grid. This system is little used today, but the diagram will help to explain circuits given later. When one end of the secondary swings negative, the other end is positive. For the next half-cycle, this is reversed.

Figure 126 has a center-tapped secondary. For one half-cycle V1 receives a negative signal, but V2 a positive signal. So V1 passes less anode current, and V2 more plate current. During the next half-cycle the opposite occurs so that V1 current increases and V2 current falls.

The 'half outputs' from V1 and V2 go to the output transformer primary. They are combined and work the speaker, connected to secondary S. This is called 'push-pull'. We can also provide so much bias that plate current is nearly cut off except when a tube grid receives a positive signal voltage. This is called 'Class B' operation, and is less drain on the supply.

125. Audio transformer for coupling

primary   secondary

126. Push-pull circuit

V1

P

bias

S

HT+

S

V2

Resistance Capacity Coupling can be employed instead. In Figure 127, V1 receives audio signals at G1. When its plate current rises, the voltage drop in R1 and R2 increases. So point X swings negative, and Y swings positive. The result is like using a center-tapped transformer to supply V2 and V3. Signals go via C1 and C2. R3 and R4 are grid resistors. R5 supplies cathode bias.

Negative Feedback

We can take part of the output signal and return it to *oppose* the original signal. This reduces distortion. Components such as capacitors have varying effects as frequency changes. Suppose the amplifier gives most amplification to high tones, or has too much 'top'. If we feed back signals to oppose the input, these top frequencies will be most strongly present. This will reduce high frequencies more than lower frequencies. The overall result is better 'fidelity', or faithfulness of amplification. In Figure 128, feedback is through R1 to the tube cathode.

127 Push-pull circuit from a typical amplifier

128 Negative feedback

Transistor Audio Amplifier

Figure 129 has TR1 as audio amplifier. R1 and R2 are chosen so that a small base current flows and the PNP transistor base is slightly more negative than the emitter. R3 stabilizes the working conditions by emitter bias. If current rises, more voltage is lost in R3. So the emitter is more negative. This lowers the base-to-emitter voltage and reduces current. C1 by-passes R3 at working frequency.

Changes in base current from the signal source cause changes in collector current. These develop a signal voltage across the load resistor R4. C2 has low reactance at audio frequencies, so signals arrive at the base of the second transistor TR2. Because of C2 the circuit is called 'capacitor coupled'. TR2 gives further amplification.

In Figure 130, potentials on TR1 collector and TR2 base are arranged to be the same, so that they can be directly connected. This is 'direct coupling'.

Figure 131 has three stages of amplification, all directly coupled. The collector voltages on TR1 and TR2 will be low, but can be sufficient for good results.

130 Direct coupling of collector to base

131 Direct coupling for miniature deaf aid

Car Radio

Figure 132 is a typical car radio amplifier. The output transistor needs a large current, but can work directly from a 12 volt battery. Only one transistor is present. It must amplify the whole audio cycle. This is termed Class A operation.

Speaker matching is by a tapped winding, instead of a transformer with separate primary and secondary. Such a tapped component is an 'auto-transformer'.

132 Car radio Class A ouput stage

Push-Pull Too

'Class B' working with transistors uses base bias which causes collector current to be lower than with 'Class A'. Figure 133 has resistors R1 and R2 to supply the bases of TR1 and TR2 through the transformer secondary. When audio signals drive TR1 into the conducting region for one half-cycle, collector current rises. For the other half-cycle TR2 is made to conduct [134]. This is the same as using electron tubes in push-pull. Battery drain is small at low volume, or when no signal is present, but rises to allow adequate loudspeaker volume when required.

Figure 135 shows an arrangement often found in miniature transistor receivers. The transformer has two secondaries, each driving one transistor. The transistors conduct on alternate halves of the signal cycle. No output transformer is needed, and a miniature 8 ohm or other speaker can be fed directly.

Stereophonic Amplifier

A stereo amplifier [136] has two channels. Volume control VR1 takes off the required signal level from a stereo pick-

133 Transistor TR1 base driven so TR1 conducts

R1

TR1

TR2

R2

R3

134 Transistor TR2 base driven so TR2 conducts

TR1

TR2

S

speaker

135 A 'single-ended' push-pull output stage

up, which supplies right-hand and left-hand outputs. Signals pass through R1 and R2 to V1A. V1A and V1B are assemblies of a triode-tetrode. R4 is the plate load, and C3 couples to the control grid of V1B. R5 and R8 with by-pass capacitors C2 and C5 provide cathode bias. R7 and C4 drop and smooth the supply for V1A. Transformer T couples to the speaker. Higher frequencies pass back through C6 and R9 to the junction of R2 and R3, to provide selective feedback controlled by VR2, for adjusting treble.

The left-hand channel output of the pick-up goes to a second identical amplifier, and to the left-hand speaker. A common power pack supplies both amplifiers, and the equipment is generally assembled on a single chassis.

During the recording, right- and left-hand channels depend on strength according to the position of the musical instruments or performers, and so a person listening to the speakers in Figure 136 obtains a sensation of depth. (See also page 104). A similar effect is obtained when listening to stereo broadcasts. Special means are used to provide right- and left-hand channels.

136 Amplifier and system for stereo reproduction

137. Long wire antenna

138. Frame antenna

earth

windings

rod

VC1   139. Loop-stick antenna

How a Radio Receiver Works

Radio waves travel 300 million meters a second, with the electromagnetic field and the electrostatic field at right angles. We speak of 'wave length' or 'frequency'. If the wave changes from positive to negative and back 300,000 times a second, there will be 1,000 meters from the crest of one wave to the next. So a wave length of 1,000 meters equals a frequency of 300,000 cycles per second (c/s).

1,000c/s = 1 kilocycle, 1kc/s, or 1 kilo Hertz

1,000m = 300kc/s

1,000kc/s = 1 megacycle, 1Mc/s, or 1MHz.

A long wire can intercept part of the radio wave [37]. A signal voltage across the coil L1 induces a voltage in the coil L2, which is tuned by the variable capacitor VC1 to select the desired frequency.

Portable receivers may use a frame antenna [138]. The wave induces a signal voltage in the winding, which is tuned to the desired station by VC1. Small portables generally have a loop-stick antenna [139]. A winding is tuned by VC1. A smaller coupling winding X-X supplies a transistor.

140. Dipole for TV, VHF, etc.

Frame and loop-stick antennas are directive. They pick up signals best when an imaginary axis through the windings is at right angles to the direction of the transmitter. Pick-up is least when the axis points to the transmitter. This is used in direction-finding equipment. (See also page 122).

Television and Very High Frequency
Television and very high frequency (VHF) transmissions are of very short wave length, and so a dipole can be used [140]. It is about the same length as a half-wave. It is cut at the center and a 75 ohm co-axial or twin feeder connected. This carries signal currents to the coil L1.

A slightly longer element or 'reflector' can be put behind the dipole. This increases signal strength. Shorter elements or 'directors' may be positioned in front of the dipole. The elements may be arranged like an H, or an X.

Adding a reflector and directors changes the center impedance of the dipole, making it low. Therefore it is folded and the feeder is attached to X-X. The antenna has its elements placed vertically and horizontally to match the 'polarization' of the television or VHF signal.

75

Resonance

Radio transmitters use different frequencies. To choose a signal we tune a circuit to 'resonance' with it. Figure 141 is a parallel-tuned circuit. The 'resonant frequency' is that at which a signal voltage is developed across the coil. Altering the capacity VC1 changes the resonant frequency. VC1 is operated by a drive having a dial marked with frequencies, stations, or wavelengths.

With a fixed coil L1, moving VC1 from minimum to maximum capacity covers a band of frequencies. One band is about 1,500kc to 600kc, or 200 to 500 meters (medium waves). For other wavebands, we select coils of different size and inductance. Figure 142 has S1 to select L1 or L2. Other coils can be present.

Often the coils have other windings, such as the coupling primaries. Then section S2 can choose these at the same time. A receiver may have several coils and a switch with a number of sections.

We may tune two or more circuits at once. Figure 143 has the antenna coil with primary P1 and secondary S1,

141. Parallel tuned current

142. Selecting different
bands of frequency

143 Ganged tuning

144. Adjustable trimmers and cores

tuned by VC1. Amplified signals go to Y and to the primary P2. The secondary S2 is tuned by VC2. The ganged capacitor VC1—VC2 has two sets of plates with a single spindle. In some receivers, VC1 and VC2 both tune the same frequency—that of the transmission wanted. Two tuned circuits make the receiver more 'selective': we can better choose or select one station from others on near frequencies.

In superhet receivers, VC2 tunes to a different frequency. By a process called heterodyning or beating all stations produce a signal of the same frequency. Later circuits can be permanently tuned to this new frequency.

Often each coil has an adjustable core [144]. Its inductance can be matched with other coils. Coils generally have a trimmer T1. This compensates for stray circuit capacity in wiring, tubes, transistors, etc. The technician adjusts cores and trimmers so that the circuits 'gang' as exactly as possible together.

carrier wave

modulated

demodulated

145 The process of demodulation

audio

diode

L1 VC1 C1 audio

146 A diode demodulator

Demodulation

Putting the audible program into the radio wave is called 'modulation'. Recovering the sound from the signal is 'demodulation' or 'detection'. A radio wave with no modulation is of uniform strength [145]. Many broadcasts use 'amplitude' modulation. A radio wave modulated with a single tone is represented, but for speech and music the shape is very complicated. The modulated wave reaches a diode in the receiver. This lets current pass one way only, and so removes one-half of the modulated waves, as shown in the diagram.

The peaks of the radio signals are smoothed by later circuits, leaving a copy of the audio signal used to modulate the transmitted signal. In Figure 146 L1 is tuned to the desired station by VC1. Signal voltages resemble the 'modulated' wave. The diode produces the 'demodulated' wave. Capacitor C1 helps smooth the radio frequency peaks to produce the audio output. This could be heard with headphones, but as a rule will pass to an amplifier. When the signals are strong, enough output is obtained from the diode to work headphones [147]. This is the simple crystal radio receiver, similar in performance to the crystal sets so popular in the early days of radio. Semiconductor diodes were not then made, but an efficient detector consisted of a crystal, and cat's-whisker of thin wire. This resembled the point contact diode.

In tube receivers, a thermionic diode often provides demodulation. The heated cathode emits electrons, and the diode conducts from cathode to plate only [148]. The audio signal is developed across R1, and taken from C2 to an amplifier. L1 is usually the secondary of an 'intermediate frequency transformer'. The diode is generally part of a diode-triode or duo-diode-triode tube. The triode section is used for audio amplification. C1 is a radio frequency by-pass capacitor.

Nearly all receivers are 'superhets'—abbreviated from 'super-heterodyne'. In a superhet, an oscillator generates

147 A crystal diode receiver

148. Thermionic tube diode as demodulator

79

a signal which is made to beat with, or heterodyne received signals. This beating produces a fixed intermediate frequency, which passes to an amplifier with fixed tuned circuits. The frequencies are above audibility.

In Figure 149 the station desired is tuned in by L1 and VC1. L2 is an oscillator coil, tuned by VC2. If two frequencies are mixed, another frequency produced is equal to the difference. Suppose L1 is tuned to 200kc/s and L2 to 670kc/s. The difference is 470kc/s. Should L1 be adjusted to 1,400kc/s, and L2 to 1,870kc/s, the difference is still 470kc/s. By arranging that the *difference* between L1 and L2 frequencies remains unchanged, the same frequency output is obtained.

Figure 150 is a transistor mixer. L1 is tuned to the desired transmission. L2 transfers the signals to the base B. L3 is the oscillator coil, with windings connected to collector C and emitter E. R3 is for emitter bias.

If L1 tunes from 500kc/s to 1,500kc/s for medium waves, and the later stages are to operate at 470kc/s, then L3 tunes from 970kc/s to 1,970kc/s. The *ratio* of frequencies covered by L3 (970:1,970) is smaller than frequencies covered by L1 (500: 1,500) so VC2 is smaller, or has a capacitor C in series.

The desired frequency from the mixer is the 'intermediate frequency'. It is often around 455kc/s to 470kc/s, but much higher in receivers for high frequencies.

Switching can select other coils, for more wavebands [151]. Each coil can have its own trimmer and adjustable core.

Some receivers have a radio frequency amplifier before the mixer [152]. This is tuned to the desired station frequency ('signal frequency'). Tube receivers operate in a similar way, with the circuit arranged for tubes.

When signals have been converted to a chosen fixed frequency, they pass to the 'intermediate frequency' amplifier. Signals have been converted from radio frequency to this intermediate frequency. Later they will become a lower, audio frequency.

149. What a superhet mixer does

any frequency

single frequency

in

out

L2
L1 VC1
VC2

150. Transistor mixer

R1
C
B
E
L2
R2
R3
VC1
L1
L3
C
VC2

151. Switching for other wavebands

MW
LW
C
B
MW
MW
medium
wave
LW
long
wave
MW
LW
MW
E
LW

152. Radio frequency amplifier

loop-stick antenna

base

81

IF Amplifier

The intermediate frequency transformer IFT1 [153] is permanently tuned to the intermediate frequency. After amplification by transistor TR1, signals pass to IFT2, then to transistor TR2. Each transistor has base supplies at X and Y. IFT3 feeds the demodulator diode D1. Audio signals are obtained across the volume control VR1. The sliding contact takes off audio signals as required.

Transformers, used to couple tubes, transistors, or other

153 Intermediate frequency amplifier

154 Intermediate frequency transformer

circuits, generally have two windings [154]. Each is permanently tuned by a fixed capacitor C. The cores are screwed in or out, allowing changes in inductance and precise adjustment to the correct frequency. Often the diode winding is not tuned [IFT3, Figure 153]. In some receivers, none of the secondaries is tuned.

A transistor can provide demodulation [155]. Audio signals are taken off through capacitor C. Thermionic diodes, triodes, and other tubes can be used as detectors. A semiconductor diode is very popular.

Figure 156 shows the stages of a receiver. The mixer converts all incoming signals to one frequency. The intermediate frequency amplifier tuned circuits help eliminate possible interference from other transmissions, and also raise the signal strength. The detector recovers the audio signal. But this signal is not yet strong enough to operate a loudspeaker and must be raised in level by the audio amplifier. The output stage or last amplifier increases the power even more, and signal strength becomes great enough to drive the loudspeaker. The same sequence of stages is often used in a tube receiver.

155. Transistor detector

156. Block diagram of a superhet receiver

How a Television Receiver Works

The television station transmits two signals—one for audio and one for video. It would be possible to use separate receivers and antennas, one for audio and the other for picture reception [157].

But sound and picture frequencies are near each other, so we may employ the same antenna. We can also build the equipment as a single receiver, and employ some sections for both audio and video [158]. A radio frequency amplifier increases the strength of both audio and video signals, which are then separated. A common power pack provides current for both sound and picture sections.

TV Sound

The sound program may be provided by amplitude modulation of the carrier wave. The apparent strength of the wave changes with the audio signals—speech or music, etc. A detector recovers the sound, as with radio.

Sound can also be provided by frequency modulation.

157. Television—audio and video

158. Circuits combined in a TV receiver

159. Some TV channels showing adjacent sound and picture frequencies

Channel	Megacycles
2	54–60
3	60–66
4	66–72
5	76–82
6	82–88
7	174–180
8	180–186
9	186–192
10	192–198
11	198–204
12	204–210
13	210–216
UHF	470–890

160. Antennas are made for the channels required

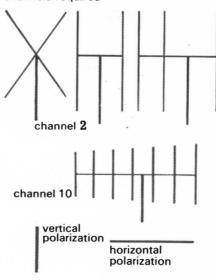

channel 2

channel 10

vertical polarization

horizontal polarization

The amplitude of the wave remains the same, but its frequency is changed to carry audio signals. The sound is recovered by a 'ratio detector' or other frequency modulation detector. FM is used for television sound.

Frequencies

The frequency or wavelength determines the channel, just as in sound broadcasting [159]. As already mentioned, each station has two adjacent frequencies—one for sound, and one for video. We usually select the station by some form of rotary or other preset tuning arrangement, to which a variable fine tuner may be added.

The antenna is arranged to suit the channel we want, or we may have a combined antenna for two or more frequencies. The receiver antenna elements must be vertical or horizontal, in order to suit the 'polarization' of the signals [160], depending on the transmitter.

Figure 161 shows circuits we can use for sound reception. The radio frequency amplifier passes signals to the converter. This fulfills the same purpose as in a radio receiver, and converts signals to the intermediate frequency, to be handled by an IF amplifier of fixed tuning. The IF amplifier first stage is common to both audio and video circuits. The outputs of this amplifier are separated. Sound signals pass to a further IF amplifier, used for sound only, then to a demodulator or detector, audio amplifier, output stage and loudspeaker.

161 Circuits in use for sound-reception

162 Turret tuner unit
antenna
RF amplifier
oscillator
mixer
to IF amplifier

163 Rotating turreturret
rotating turret with inductors
fine tuning
contacts
tubes
turret knob
locating mechanism

86

We probably want to receive signals from two widely separated channels. For some changes in frequency we can switch different coils or inductances into circuit. Figure 162 shows a VHF tuner circuit. It has a radio frequency amplifier, followed by a mixer and covers a number of frequencies by switching inductors.

The tuner has a turret [163] with a number of inductances set around a shaft. Any of the inductors can be brought into circuit by rotating a control knob. This has a similar effect to the bandswitching seen in radio receivers, but is more efficient.

For ultra high frequencies (UHF) switching is too inefficient: VHF and UHF tuners are used. The VHF tuner, with its own antenna, accepts signals from the desired station in this band. The UHF tuner operates with its own antenna, and selects the higher frequency transmissions.

Signals from either tuner can be passed on to the intermediate frequency amplifier.

164 Tuned circuits separate the sound and vision signals

Separator
Figure 164 is a combined audio and video amplifier. Sound signals are separated from video signals by the transformer. This separation is possible because the sound and video signals are on different frequencies. Both were mixed with a single common frequency in the oscillator. So the output from the mixer is one frequency for sound, and another for video.

165. Scanning the picture area

166. Cathode ray beam forming a picture

167. Interlaced scanning and use of more lines

interlacing

many lines

few lines

Forming a Picture

The picture is formed by a spot of light moving over the tube screen, and increasing or reducing in intensity to make light and dark areas. Covering the screen face in regular lines is called 'scanning'.

In Figure 165 we scan the picture area by starting the spot at A and moving it to B, then flashing it back instantly to C, and moving it along again to D. This is continued until we end at E. From here, the spot returns to A, to begin again.

If we use many lines they lie closely one above the other. By controlling the spot brightness, and covering the whole area many times a second [166], we build up a complete picture.

The television receiver screen is fluorescent, glowing under the influence of the cathode ray. There is only one small area where the cathode ray strikes the screen at any instant. Persistence of the tube coating, which glows for a short time after the spot has passed, makes the whole screen appear to be illuminated.

Interlaced scanning of alternate lines is used to avoid flickering [167].

It is important that there should be a large number of lines.

If there are few lines the spot area is large and the picture cannot have much detail. A picture made from 405 line signals has less detail than one from a 525 line signal (exaggerated in Figure 167). Some of the line periods are employed for synchronization.

With interlaced scanning, the whole picture area is covered by 262.5 lines. This is a 'frame' and occupies $\frac{1}{30}$ second. The remaining lines cover the screen, filling the spaces between those in the first frame during another $\frac{1}{30}$ second. The field is thus completed in $\frac{1}{60}$ second, since there are two frames per field.

To obtain a picture, the movement of the spot must agree with that of the scanning beam in the camera supplying picture signals. This is arranged by synchronizing pulses [168].

The television receiver circuits are adjusted for approximately the correct scanning speed. At the end of each line a line synchronizing pulse occurs, and triggers the receiver line-scan circuit. At the end of the frame, a series of pulses triggers the frame-scanning circuit, returning the spot to the beginning of its travel over the picture area.

signal controlling spot brightness

line sync. pulses

168. Synchronization of scanning signal controlling spot brightness

How the Scan is Produced

The cathode ray tube cathode emits electrons focused into a narrow beam. This beam strikes the tube face, causing fluorescence. Magnetic deflection is by coils [169]. Current in two coils deflects the spot from side to side. Current in the other coils moves the spot up or down. They are 'line' and 'frame' scan coils according to purpose.

A rapid sawtooth wave [170] produces line scanning. Rise X causes deflection of the spot. It traces a line across the screen. Flyback (return) of the spot Y to a new line is fast. Voltage rises again after each flyback.

For frame scanning, a slower sawtooth is needed (not shown to scale in Figure 170). Z1 carries the spot smoothly down the screen. After about half the total number of lines, the bottom is reached. The spot flies up to the top, due to the abrupt change Y1. It descends smoothly again during Z2, and returns to the top again during Y2.

169. Paris of coils used to scan picture area

pairs of coils at
right angles

170. Line scan and frame scan waves

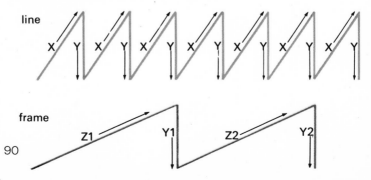

line

X Y X Y X Y X Y X Y X Y X Y

frame

Z1 Y1 Z2 Y2

Video Signals

The video signal goes to the video IF amplifier, and is increased in strength [171]. Various parts of the signal have to perform specific functions.

Line synchronizing pulses present with the signal synchronize the line oscillator as described, so each line begins at the correct instant. Frame pulses synchronize the frame generator.

Video signals control the intensity of the spot during its motion, to build up the picture light and shade. The vision or video detector may be a semiconductor diode [172]. Its output passes to an amplifier. The video signal then controls the intensity of the beam, and thus the brilliance of the spot as it travels over the screen.

Figure 173 is a frame oscillator to generate the sawtooth output which deflects the spot. We adjust the oscillator frequency with the frame hold control. If the frequency

171 Important vision circuits of receiver

172 Vision detector vision amplifier and tube

91

173 Frame generator

height

frame coils

HP+

output

sync. pulses

frame hold

174 Heaters and power supply

cathode ray tube

tubes

R1 voltage selection

house current

is too far from the sync pulses, these cannot control the scanning, and the picture breaks up. The frequency of the line scan is also adjusted until it can be synchronized by the line sync pulses.

Power Supplies

TV receivers have many tubes, so the heaters are usually connected in series [174]. The voltage needed is the total of all tubes added together, and is made up to the house current voltage by resistor R1. Another tapped resistor allows adjustment for 200 volt to 250 volt supplies. This is economical with a large number of valves, but the chassis is 'hot' (has a potential on it).

High power for most stages of the receiver is obtained with a tube or other rectifier giving 200 volts or so.

The cathode ray tube requires a very high power supply of some kilovolts obtained from the line scan circuit [175].

92

175 Extra high tension for the tube obtained from line scan circuit

176 A TV receiver circuit

V1 is the line output tube, and the tapped winding L1 supplies current to the line coils, to deflect the cathode ray. During flyback, a high e.m.f. is produced in this winding, for the high power rectifier V2. Current from the small winding L2 heats this tube.

Output from V2 may be smoothed by a high voltage capacitor. Or the tube can have inner and outer coatings, separated by glass and acting as a capacitor. Rectification in V3 boosts the supply; hence the voltage at V1 plate is higher than the B + supply.

Essential sections of a television receiver are in Figure 176. The tuner selects the station and converts to the intermediate frequency. IF, detector, audio and output stages provide sound. The video intermediate frequency amplifier, detector and amplifier control the strength of the cathode ray. Pulses synchronize line and frame oscillators, whose outputs go to the deflection coils. High B + is from the line amplifier, low B + from a power pack.

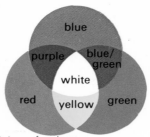

177. Additive mixing of colors
178. A method of obtaining color signals for transmission

Color Television

Colors other than black can be made up by mixing three chosen colors. The additive combination of light differs from results obtained with pigments. Absence of all colors forms black. Red and green together provide yellow. Blue and red give purple, and blue and green provide blue-green [177]. When red, blue and green are present in an intensity of 40 percent, 26 percent and 34 percent, combining them provides white.

To transmit a color picture, the scene is scanned by cameras sensitive to three colors, which are reproduced in the receiver. Other colors are reproduced by changing the intensity of the red, blue and green channels.

Figure 178 is a color camera system. Mirror A lets red pass, but reflects blue and green. B reflects green but transmits blue, which is reflected by C. In this way the scene scanned is separated into the three colors, each providing its own signal. Other arrangements of selective mirrors

94

may be used in order to obtain the desired result. The picture could be reproduced by three projection tubes, one each for red, green and blue, and each receiving the red, green or blue signal [179].

A shadow mask color tube has three separate cathode assemblies [180]. Each emits a ray controlled by the red, green or blue channels. A mask with many small holes is fitted inside the tube. The cathode rays come from slightly different directions, and after passing through the same hole strike different spots on the screen. The screen is coated so that rays from the blue channel gun strike areas producing blue. The cathode ray responsible for green strikes areas which produce green, and in the same way the red-producing ray strikes areas which cause red. The different color spots are so small that the eye blends them together into the various desired shades. Deflection coils move the three cathode rays over the tube face together.

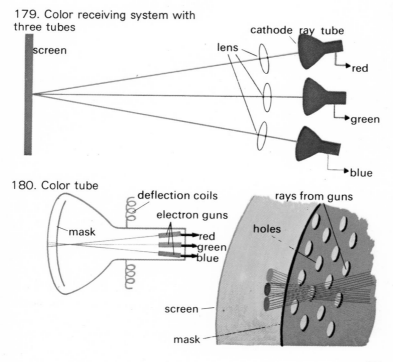

179. Color receiving system with three tubes

screen lens cathode ray tube

red

green

blue

180. Color tube

deflection coils

electron guns

mask

red
green
blue

rays from guns

holes

screen

mask

Recording on Tape, and Disc Stereo

Tape recordings are much used for video or television picture recording, input and storage of computer information, and other purposes.

For sound recording, the signal level is raised with an audio amplifier [181], and taken to a recording head that has a winding and magnetic core with a narrow gap. Signals in the winding cause a fluctuating magnetic field across this gap.

The tape is polyvinyl chloride or other insulating material, coated on one side with tiny particles of iron oxide. It is often ¼ in. wide for sound, and 2 ins. for video.

181. Amplification and recording head

The unused tape has magnetic particles lying at random [182]. A mechanism draws the tape smoothly by the head gap. The particles are brought into magnetic alignment, and the tape has magnetized areas corresponding to the audio currents in the head winding.

For longer playing time, about half the track is used with the tape passing one way, and the remaining half with the tape reversed. Quarter-track recording is also used.

Frequency Response

Suppose the tape moves 15 ins. per second and a 15 cycle per second audio tone is recorded. There will be 1 in. tape

magnetic
particles

audio tone

tape drawn over gap ⟶

particles aligned

full track

portion used

half track

quarter track

182. Magnetic recording on tape

length from one cycle peak to the next. If the tape moves at 7½ ips the distance would fall to ½ in. For slower tape speeds, the distance between peaks becomes smaller [183]. Raising the audio frequency also brings the magnetized sections closer to each other.

A limit arises when the magnetic 'domain' length from one cycle to the next is smaller than the gap of the head. Then results soon fall off. To help avoid this limit, head gaps are very small—as small as 0.00025 in.

For music, or when a response up to 10,000cps or so will be wanted, the tape may move at 15 ips, while 7½ ips and 3¾ in. per second speeds suit less exacting needs, and 1⅞ ins. per second or slower movement allows satisfactory recording of speech, and gives long playing time with small reels. Two or more tracks also give longer time.

The tape is drawn by a 'capstan', a revolving roller. It may have a heavy flywheel and belt drive [184].

183. Tape speed and frequency response   184. Tape driving mechanism

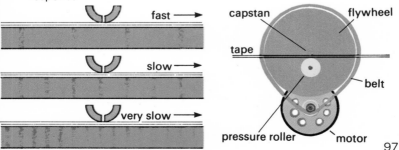

fast ⟶

slow ⟶

very slow ⟶

capstan   flywheel

tape

belt

pressure roller   motor

97

Playback

To hear the recording, the tape is wound on its original reel, then drawn past a playback head at the same speed as when recorded [185]. The magnetized tape causes a small magnetic field in the head core, thus generating an electrical output. When recording, audio currents produce a varying magnetic field; during playback, the varying of the magnetic field causes audio currents.

In many spheres, such as broadcasting, news gathering and so on, signals may be recorded from sources other than a microphone (e.g., from other tape recordings, from discs or from radio programs). Signals can also be recorded from television so that playback supplies a picture. Equipment for this is complicated.

For house current use, recorders can employ about four stages, resistance capacity coupled [186]. For better volume and fidelity, push-pull output may be provided.

Record/Playback

The same head may be used to record on the tape, and obtain signals when playing the recording. Switching of input

185. Playback of the recording

186. Vacuum tube playback

and output circuits allows the same amplifier to be employed for both purposes [187]. With the switch at R (Record) the microphone provides the amplifier input.

For playback (P) the head is switched to the amplifier input, and the output to a loudspeaker. There are two 'outputs', because that for the head is taken from an earlier stage—the full power of a large amplifier is not used while recording.

Recording Level Indicator
An indicator shows us that recording is at a suitable level. In Figure 188, X goes to an audio amplifier. The diode rectifies audio signals, building up a negative voltage. This reduces plate current, so the deflector plates become more positive. Electrons from the cathode strike a target, and the beam width is controlled by the deflector plate potential. Hence the display depends on the average audio power, and we adjust volume for correct recording.

If we apply a high frequency 'bias' oscillation to the head while recording, results are improved. The power output stage can be utilized as a bias oscillator. In Figure 189, C1

187. Recorder/playback switching R=record
microphone P=playback

amplifier
input   output
output

R
speaker
P

head R
P

188. Recording level indicator

B+

470K   target

0.01 µF

X

deflector

470K

0.05
µF

6.8 MΩ

99

189. High frequency bias oscillator

B+

speaker

C1

bias oscillator coil

erase

G1

C2

R1

to head

couples the oscillator coil, and feedback to G1 sustains oscillation. HF bias is taken through C2 and R1 to the recording head.

To erase a recording, the particles are restored to random orientation. Permanent magnet systems can remove a recording, but a high frequency erase signal is better. The bias oscillator provides a stronger signal, output being from the whole secondary [190]. The tape is drawn past the erasing head, and the rapidly alternating field shifts the magnetic particles into random positions.

The playback head output is not uniform over a wide frequency range, but peaks around 2,500 cycles [191]. Fixed or variable tone control or correction circuits help flatten out response. In figure 191, C1 has low reactance at high fre-

190 Erasing an old recording

erase head

tape

191 Frequency characteristic and tone control circuit

quency, while C2 bypasses high frequencies; thus rotating VR3 allows treble to be adjusted.

Transistor Equipment
Figure 192 is a 'pocket' recorder. During recording (R) the microphone supplies signals through C1. Amplified signals reach the head through R1. During playback (P) the head supplies signals through C1, output being to a small speaker. VR1 is for volume control.

There is no HF or erase bias. Erasure is obtained by a permanent magnet, which swamps out the selective orientation of particles during recording. A low-consumption 6 volt motor provides power to drive the capstan. C2 suppresses motor noise.

192 Transistor tape recorder

193 Tape transport

reels

tape

free-wheel
release drive

spool wheel

counter

belts

capstan

flywheel

motor

194 A two-speed mechanism

1st position

idle friction
wheel

2nd position

driving shaft

Drive Mechanism

Figure 193 is a drive mechanism. (Other methods are used.) Here, one motor performs all functions. During recording or playback, a puck wheel keeps the tape in contact with the capstan, and winds it at uniform speed past the head. At the same time, the wheel on which the take-up reel rests turns at the correct speed to take up tape.

To move the tape the other way (for multi-track recording), the motor is reversed, and a free-wheel transfers the drive to the other reel. For fast rewinding on the original reel the puck wheel is withdrawn, and the take-up reel revolves at full speed. A belt from one reel wheel drives a mechanical counter, which enables starting positions to be noted.

Figure 194 is a speed-change mechanism, allowing a higher speed to be used for music or high fidelity, and a lower speed for speech or longer playing time.

A series of push-buttons often control operation, and may energize 2-pole change-over switching contacts [195]. Any button depressed is held by a spring load common to all buttons. Such switching can change heads, for upper or lower tracks on a tape, and reverse the motor, etc. Many electro-mechanical devices are often used in electronics. One such is a solenoid which pulls a roller, to press tape against the rotating capstan [196]. When no current flows through the solenoid, the tape is free for rapid winding.

195. Push-button control and heads for two tracks

196. Solenoid-operated tape transport

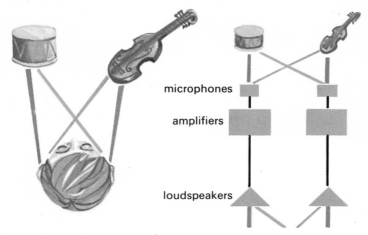

Stereo Reproduction

Stereophonic sound appears to have direction and depth, as we can realize when we hear a live orchestral performance. The effect depends on changes in strength and phase of sounds from different directions [197].

The same effect can be obtained by using two microphones, amplifiers and loudspeakers. A person between the loudspeakers near the third corner of a triangle, the loudspeakers occupying the other corners, seems to hear a live performance.

Stereo disc records have two channels, for right and left, cut in one groove and obtained from right- and left-hand microphones, or directional microphones.

The stereo pick-up stylus can vibrate in two directions. Vibration one way changes the magnetic field in a coil for

198. Stereo from discs

the right-hand output. The other direction produces the left-hand output. Each output goes to its own amplifier and loudspeaker [198].

For stereo tape two or four tracks supply separate left- and right-hand channels [199]. Recording is from two sources and amplifiers. Playback is simultaneously from both tracks, with individual amplifiers and speakers.

For best results, stereo equipment may have high fidelity amplifiers—circuits able to give equal tonal results with little distortion over a wide frequency range.

Video Tape Recording

Frequencies to be retained when recording a television picture are very much higher than those encountered with sound. With the normal type of tape recorder, the tape speed would have to be impracticably high.

A method of overcoming this speed is to employ heads equally displaced on the perimeter of a rotating wheel. As a tape ¾ in., 1 in., or 2 ins. wide passes across the heads the recorded video tracks lie at an angle [200].

Tape speeds depend on the purpose, but may be 15 ins. per second or 7½ ins. per second, and the latter used with rotating heads gives an effective speed of 75 ft. per second.

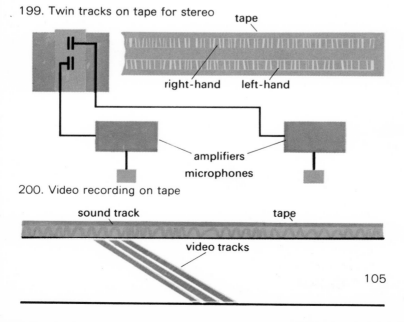

199. Twin tracks on tape for stereo

tape

right-hand   left-hand

amplifiers

microphones

200. Video recording on tape

sound track   tape

video tracks

OTHER APPLICATIONS OF ELECTRONICS

Counting Electronically

Counting circuits record the number of objects produced by a machine, the number of oscillations each second, or speed, or distance. They also show the results of addition, and other operations.

Mechanical Counter

An odometer shows miles covered. An electricity meter counter shows units consumed. Seeing what actually happens mechanically is useful.

Revolving mechanical counters are often used [201]. Shaft A rotates to display numbers up to 9. When it has rotated from zero to the 10th unit, tooth X rotates the wheel on shaft B one place, moving the tens counter from 0 to 1. This happens with each revolution of A. One complete turn of B rotates the hundreds counter one place, and 99 revolutions of shaft A, counting up to 999, can be accommodated.

A solenoid, pawl and toothed wheel could rotate shaft A. An electrical circuit closes, current flows, and the pawl moves the counter one place. Such devices are occasionally connected after high-speed electronic counters, to record very large numbers.

What actually happens? As shown in Figure 202, each time the full 'units' capacity is reached, one impulse is transferred to the 'tens' counter and the units return to zero.

201. Mechanical counter

solenoid

hundreds   tens   units

202 Sequence of counter

Similarly, the full capacity of tens results in one impulse being transferred to the 'hundreds' position.

Electronic circuits giving one output pulse for a number of input pulses similarly form a section of a counter.

Mechanical processes that are repeated can be counted by a closing circuit [203]. The counter is electrically operated. Current from the supply reaches the solenoid each time the circuit closes, moving the units counter. The switch may be operated by weight, or by any means.

Electronic methods perform the same function more reliably, easily and rapidly. Figure 204 has an infra-red light beam falling on a photocell. This causes an electrical output which is amplified. When the beam is interrupted an impulse is passed to the units counter. Every tenth impulse is transferred to the tens counter, and so on.

203. Electro-mechanical counter   204. Electronic counter

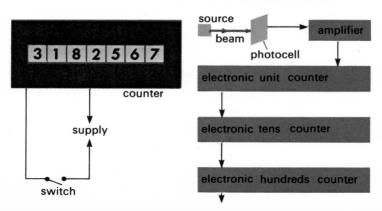

A ring counter gives one output pulse for a selected number of input pulses—for the decimal system, one output pulse for ten input pulses [205]. We may use controlled rectifiers, thyratrons or other devices which remain stable until 'triggered' by an input pulse, retaining the new state until returned to the original.

Pulses reach the rectifiers through diodes D. Diodes except the first have a large bias voltage from the associated controlled rectifier. So the first pulse triggers only the first rectifier. This one conducts, causing a low voltage across the second diode. Hence the next pulse can trigger the second controlled rectifier, and ten pulses progress along the circuit. The last rectifier gives an output pulse to a 'tens' panel, and back to the input to restore the units circuit to zero. Six panels would count up to 999,999.

205 A ring counter

controlled rectifiers (10 in all)

D   D   D   D   D

input   output

Trochotron and Dekatron

The trochotron has a central cathode, ten grids, ten targets or plates, and ten electrodes [206]. Grids 1, 3, 5, 7 and 9 are connected to one circuit, and 2, 4, 6, 8 and 0 to another circuit. Suppose the electron stream is at 0. An input pulse cuts off the stream, while grid 1 causes the beam to form on target 1. Each subsequent pulse moves the beam around one step. The final position can transfer one pulse to a 'tens' counting tube. The trochotron can count one million a *second*.

The dekatron has ten cathodes. Ionization causes the

discharge path to glow [207]. The X pins are joined and fed from pulses to be counted. Pulses reach the Y pins through a delay circuit. When a pulse pin X near 7 deflects the discharge clockwise, a further deflection arises as the delayed pulse reaches adjacent pin Y. When the pulse ceases, the discharge has been stepped to 8. This can be repeated as many times as required.

206 The trochotron has 10 electron stream positions

207 Dekatron counter

208 A tube to display numerals

Read-Out Tube

Figure 208 is a tube with electrodes in the shape of the numerals 0 to 9 arranged close together with a common plate. The other ends of the numerals are connected to separate pins. The discharge causes a visible glow around the numeral receiving voltage.

only electrode with potential glows

electrodes shaped 0 to 9

pins

109

209 Decimal and binary counters

decimal

binary

210 Decimal and binary compared

decimal
1111 objects =

			1	=	1
	1	× 10	=	10
1	× 10	× 10	=	100
1 × 10	× 10	× 10	=	1000
					1111

binary
1111 objects =

			1	=	1
	1	× 2	=	2
1	× 2	× 2	=	4
1 × 2	× 2	× 2	=	8
decimal					15

The Binary System

We need not count in the form '1, 2, 3, 4, 5, 6, 7, 8, 9, 0 and carry 1'. Electronically there are advantages in counting in other ways. The binary system counts by using 0 and 1. Figure 209 shows two counters, one with 0–9 dials and one for binary. They have rotating pointers. We record objects up to 9 on A of the decimal counter. For 10 we see there is no higher number than 9 here. So we set A to zero and transfer 1 to B. We proceed in this way to 999.

With binary the highest number on any dial is 1. When one object arrives, this is put on A, giving 000,001. For object 2 there is no number higher than 1 on A. So we restore A to 0, carrying one to B, to get 000,010. For object 3 we put A to 1 again: 000,011. The next object results in 0 for A and carry 1, 0 and carry one for B, turning C to 1 = 000,100. Similarly, 5 = 000,101; 6 = 000,110; 7 = 000,111; 8 = 001,000; 9 = 001,001, 10 = 001,010, and so on.

Each time we move to the left in decimal counting, we multiply by 10 [210]. Each move to the left in binary multiplies by 2 because there are two possibilities for each column (0 and 1). To register numbers from 0 to 9 in decimal systems, we need *ten* reliable states for an electronic device. For binary, we need *two*—for 0 to 1.

A lack of voltage or current can represent 0, and full voltage or current can show 1. The result is a definite 'on'—'off' system for each column [211].

Computers
Relays close when energized [212]. Early computers used thousands of relays. Vacuum tube plate current is low with strong negative grid bias, but high with little bias or a positive pulse. The PNP transistor does not conduct with a positive signal at the base, but conducts with a negative signal,

211 Switches acting as binary numbers

212 Relays, valves and transistors as binary numbers

213 Computers with tape input and output

and operation is only 'on' or 'off'. The computer may take input pulses from a tape, store and process them, and deliver the solution or output to a second tape [213].

Bi-Stable Multivibrator or Flip-Flop Circuit
Figure 214 shows a circuit that will remain in either of two conditions. If transistor A base is negative, transistor A collector current is large, hence collector C1 is positive, and so is base B2 of transistor B. As a result, collector C2 current is small, and there is little voltage drop across R2, and so base B1 is held negative. An input pulse reverses these conditions. Collector C1 no longer passes a large current and the voltage drop in R1 has fallen, shifting base B2 of transistor B in a negative direction. This transistor conducts, so the increased voltage drop across R2 makes collector C2 positive, and therefore base B1. The circuit thus remains in either state, until a pulse is received. Output can be taken from collector C2.

Any device which can be placed in a steady 'on' or 'off' condition can be used for counting. Binary counters divide by 2 [215]. Decade circuits divide by 10. In counting frequencies, an electronic gate (switch) allows signals to pass for a known interval, while they are counted.

Geiger counters help measure radiation intensity. A central plate of high positive potential is used in an envelope of gas mixture [216]. High velocity particles cause ionization. Liberated electrons pass to the positively charged plate, causing small output pulses.

Analog to Digital Conversion
'Analog' information represents a fact in an analogous way. A voltmeter pointer or speedometer pointer position is an analog of voltage or of miles per hour. One means of converting analog to binary digital is shown in Figure 217. A photo-electric eye registers divisions as they pass.

The second method shown has sensing devices opposite the white 0000 sectors. Black sectors are 1. Rotating the disc one step at a time produces the binary count—0001, 0010, 0011, 0100, etc.

214. Bi-stable or flip-flop circuit

215. Counters in sequence

216. A Geiger counter

217. Methods of converting analog to digital

Output-Producing Circuits

Outputs are provided by oscillators, amplifiers, and other circuits, as needed.

If an inductor L and capacitor C are in parallel [218], and a potential momentarily arises in the inductance, the inductor electromagnetic field stores energy. When the field collapses, an e.m.f. charges the capacitor. The capacitor then discharges, returning power to the inductor. Resistance and other losses cause the oscillations to get smaller and finally cease.

The oscillation frequency or 'resonant' frequency in cps

$$\text{is } \frac{1}{2\pi\sqrt{LC}}$$

where L is henrys and C farads.

Resonance occurs when inductive reactance is equal to capacitive reactance.

218. Oscillation in circuit having inductance and capacitance

Sustained Oscillation

If we add a device which cancels circuit losses, oscillation continues. Figure 219 has resonant circuit L1 and C. L2 is a coupling winding returning energy to L1. The e.m.f. across L1 reaches the control grid G. An amplified signal arises at plate A, and if L2 feeds back energy to L1 in the correct phase this sustains oscillation.

219. Positive feedback to sustain oscillation

220. Variable frequency oscillator

L2

C1

L1   VC   R1

221. Superhet receiver oscillator and mixer

amplifier

IFT

converter plate

signal received

C1

R1

L1   L2

VC

padder

A variable capacitor VC [220] allows tuning over a band of frequencies. The inductor L1 is changed for other wave-bands. Rectification between cathode and grid causes a negative charge to appear across C1 and R1, producing stable operation.

A circuit like this is found in most tube radio receivers. The oscillator is the triode part of a converter, or other mixer. Figure 221 has R1, C1, VC, L1 and L2 with the triode section. The triode grid also controls the flow of current to the converter plate. L1 is tuned so that the difference between the received signal and frequency of L1 is always the same. Mixing in the converter results in a signal of fixed frequency appearing at the plate. This output passes to the fixed tuned circuits of the intermediate frequency transformer IFT. The 'padder' helps make the coverage of L1 suitable.

115

Signal Generator

Oscillating circuits can produce a radio frequency output or radio signal. A signal generator is a source of low-power energy that we can tune to any frequency.

Figure 222 has R1 and R2 to provide suitable base working conditions, with emitter resistor R3. L1 is tuned with VC and has a feedback winding L2 to the base B. The output from the arrangement in Figure 222 is a radio frequency signal without modulation. If it is tuned in on an ordinary receiver, no sound is heard. It is termed an 'unmodulated' or 'carrier wave' output. When we need a wave modulated by an audio tone we can add an audio oscillator [223]. This modulates the RF signal. When the signal is tuned in, the audio tone is heard.

A use for the signal generator is in aligning the intermediate frequency transformers of a receiver [224]. Most IFT's

222. Tunable R-F signal generator   223. Audio modulator

have two tuned circuits, generally with adjustable cores for the coils. Trimmers could be used instead. We set the generator tuning to get the required output — often about 455kc/s. This is fed into the receiver circuit at a point ahead of the IFT circuits to be adjusted. Then we rotate the cores or trimmers with a trimming tool. Best output from the receiver shows that the circuits are suitably tuned.

The antenna and other tuned circuits in a receiver can be adjusted in this way. We set the generator to suitable frequencies, and adjust trimmers and cores so that wavelengths or frequencies are tuned in at the correct positions on the receiver dial.

Figure 225 is the radio frequency section of a signal generator for the 10–300 megacycle range, and is thus suitable for very high frequency alignment or testing.

224. Use of signal generator to align receiver

core adjusting tool

generator   output
            lead   intermediate
                   frequency
                   transformers

225. Circuit for the VHF range

low loss
coils in turret

VHF triode

Multivibrator

The 'multivibrator' circuit produces a wide range of outputs, according to working conditions. It uses two vacuum tubes, or two transistors [226]. Transistor A has collector resistor R1 and base resistor R2. B has R3 and R4. C1 couples A collector to the base of B, while C2 couples B back to the base of A. With each transistor driving the other, frequency depends largely on capacitor and resistor values. This circuit can produce outputs for receiver or amplifier testing. The multivibrator will produce both sawtooth and square waves.

Phase-Shift Oscillator

If the voltage of a PNP transistor base is moved positive, collector current falls. Less current flows in the collector resistor, less voltage is dropped here, and the collector potential moves negative. Feedback from collector to base would be in the wrong phase to sustain oscillation — negative when it should be positive, and vice versa. Two transistors, each reversing phase [226], overcome this.

So for a single transistor or vacuum tube we may need some way of reversing phase. Feedback then sustains oscillation. Capacitors and resistors can form a phase-shift circuit for this purpose [227].

Bias Oscillator

Figure 228 obtains oscillation by suitably connecting the primary P and secondary S of the oscillator coil. For example, reversing the connections to S would reverse the phase of feedback to the base. The frequency of oscillation depends on the windings and value of C1. The primary P is tapped for a suitable collector load. Output is taken from another tap through C2 to provide high frequency bias when tape recording.

Electronic Clock

Figure 229 is a circuit producing low-speed output pulses of great accuracy of occurrence. A piezo-electric crystal oscillator runs at set frequency, and this is stepped down by dividers, to obtain the low-speed output pulses used for timing. The apparatus is controlled by the crystal.

226. Multivibrator using two transistors

R1 R4 C1 C2 R2 R3 C3 output A B − +

227. Oscillator with phase-shift network

228. Tape recorder high-frequency bias oscillator

output

S P C1 C2 − +

to record head

229. An electronic clock

frequency crystal

dividers

oscillator

dividers give one output pulse for 10 input pulses

input

output

07:12 01

digital clock

230. Two cycles of a sine wave

231. Two cycles of a square wave

Waveforms

An important wave is the sine wave [230]. This is obtained
from alternating current supplies. The voltage rises smoothly
to a maximum, and falls through zero to a negative value
of equal amplitude. If we used an oscilloscope, we would
see this happening 60 times each second with 60 cycle per
second house supplies. The sine wave could be of other
frequency, perhaps a pure audio tone, from a signal generator. 'Frequency' means complete cycles per second.

The smooth rise and fall of voltage and current enables
mathematical relations to exist between the peak voltage
or current, and the effective voltage or current (which is
less). An instrument such as an AC voltmeter cannot respond to the rapid changes, and indicates the effective value.
The square wave is useful for test and other purposes. It
rises and falls almost instantaneously [231]. It can be produced by generating a sine wave and clipping positive and
negative peaks.

The sawtooth wave is quite different [232]. If a capacitor
is charged through a series resistor from a high potential

232. Sawtooth waves

233. Circuit for producing sawtooth waves

the voltage across the capacitor rises. One section, from X to Y, is fairly linear ('straight'). To produce sawtooth waves, the capacitor is discharged rapidly when it reaches Y, so the voltage falls to that at X. The capacitor charges again. This is repeated. Rise from X to Y should be without curvature. Descent to X should be almost instant.

Figure 233 shows a circuit for producing sawtooth waves. Current flows through the resistor into the capacitor, so that the charge rises (X to Y). The speed and extent of this rise can be adjusted by selecting capacitor and resistor values and the supply potential. When the charge reaches Y the switch is closed, discharging the capacitor. The switch is then opened, so the charge begins to rise again. In practical circuits, a thyratron can replace the switch. This tube conducts abruptly each time the potential reaches a pre-arranged level (see page 53).

Sawtooth waves are used in an oscilloscope. The slow rise of voltage makes the cathode ray traverse the screen, and the ray returns almost instantaneously when the capacitor is discharged, to begin another sweep.

Radar and Other Devices

Radio waves travel outward at 300 million meters or 186,000 miles per second.

So if a signal has a frequency of 300 million oscillations a second, the wave length is 1 meter [234]. The radiated signal has magnetic and electric fields at right angles. Unless reflected by the earth or bent by ionized belts, etc. the signals travel in straight lines.

A directional antenna or dish gives strongest reception of signals when pointed at the transmitter. The direction-finding receiver Rx [235a] takes bearings on transmitters Tx. These bearings on a chart cross to show the receiver position.

If the position of a transmitter Tx is not known [235b] bearings are taken from two positions. The lines cross at the transmitter.

Radio Astronomy

Observations made directly by ordinary telescope are confined to visual frequencies. Photographic time exposures record dim stars. Visible light and similar rays are absorbed

234. Speed of radio waves

300,000,000 m/s

wavelength

electric lines of force

magnetic lines

B

235. Radio direction-finding

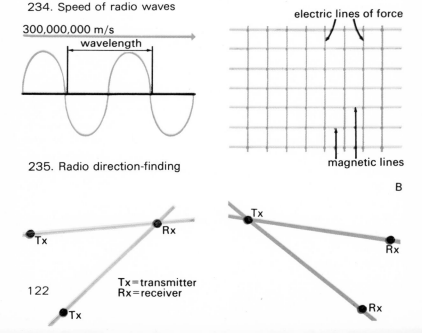

Tx

Rx

Tx

Tx=transmitter
Rx=receiver

Tx

Tx

Rx

Rx

122

about 10cm. to 10m. wavelength   236. Radio telescope

reflector

antenna

cloud
haze

recorder

mount   receiver

observed galaxies and stars

radio noise

237. Visual observation and results of radio astronomy

by haze, but radio frequency radiations are of longer wave length, and are not hindered.

Remote galaxies and systems generate radio 'noise' — that is, random bursts of radio-frequency radiation. A directive antenna can locate the bearing of these. The dish reflector [236] may be hundreds of feet in diameter, and concentrates signals on an antenna. The dish can be pivoted. Signals pass to a sensitive receiver, and are recorded. Radio noise sources are often located near systems observed optically [237]. Sources of radio noise have been mapped at enormous distances, beyond the reach of an optical telescope and where no systems can be seen or photographed. In this way, information has been gathered outside the range of optical observation. Radio waves travel 186,000 miles per second. Radio telescopes have located galaxies over 4,500 million light-years away.

antenna

transmitter
and receiver

signal —   echo

T   T   T   T

E   E   E

1 μs   2,500 μs   238. Cathode ray tube showing echo

Radio Detection And Ranging (Radar)
If aircraft are in the path of a radio signal, some energy is
reflected as an 'echo' back to the transmitter. In Figure 238
a transmitter radiates 1 micro-second pulses T of very high
frequency at 2,500μs intervals and followed by periods
in which a receiver picks up echoes E. As signals travel at·
known speed, the distance of an object is measured by noting the time taken for the echo to return. The interval can
be shown by a cathode ray traveling rapidly from left to right
across the screen [238]. A scale can be marked in distances.

Plan position radar equipment shows the distance of an
object. By rotating a directional antenna [239], and causing
the trace to scan from the center of the tube outward and
rotate with the dish, the compass bearing of an object is shown,
as well as its distance. As the antenna and trace revolve,
echoes from surrounding features build up a plan or picture
on the screen. The cathode ray may be brightened at regu-

239. Rotating dish and trace for bearing

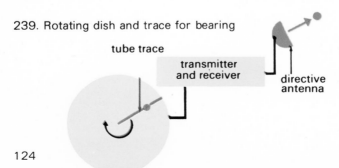

tube trace

transmitter
and receiver

directive
antenna

lar intervals to produce range rings [240]. These can be expanded or contracted at the same time as the trace speed is adjusted, to change the 'scale' so that large or small areas can be examined. Bearing marks can also be provided [240].

Some precision-approach radar for ground aid to landing aircraft has two antenna systems. One directive system sweeps a narrow beam in a horizontal plane, and the other sweeps a vertical plane [241]. The two sweeps combine to give a 3-dimensional position for an aircraft—one set of equipment produces the 2-dimensional 'map', the other the height reading, or other dimension.

240. Range and bearing marks on a plan position indicator

241. Precision-approach radar

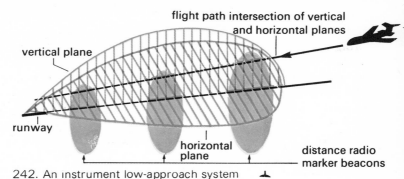

flight path intersection of vertical and horizontal planes

vertical plane

runway

horizontal plane

distance radio marker beacons

242. An instrument low-approach system

One instrument low-approach system for landing aircraft has a vertical signal to mark the runway, and a horizontal signal for the landing path. Beacons radiate vertically at 'outer', 'middle' and 'boundary' positions [242].

Sonar (Sound Navigation And Ranging) systems allow the distance to be found to the seabed and to a submerged vessel. High-frequency signals are amplified and passed to an electronic switch circuit, which directs them to a transducer [243]. Echoes are diverted to a receiver by the electronic switch, and the delay allows the cathode ray tube to give a distance reading.

Pictures by Radio (Facsimile Transmission)
News pictures can be sent across the world by radio. A picture secured to a rotating drum can be scanned electronically in lines which lie closely side by side [244]. Radio signals corresponding to light and dark areas are produced. At the receiver, a drum rotates at the same speed, and a writing head slowly moves the length of the drum, produc-

243. Sonar sound-navigation and ranging

oscillator

amplifier

switch

display on cathode ray tube

echo amplifier

transducer

ing light and dark marks. So a complete picture is built up during many rotations of the drum.

Radio signals for pictures may be tape-recorded for storage, or for re-transmission when long-distance short-wave radio conditions are suitable. To synchronize a tape, the tape can have two tracks, one for picture information, and the other recording from a crystal oscillator. These signals are amplified and applied to a synchronous motor, the speed of which depends on the frequency [245]. A second motor receives amplified signals from a second crystal oscillator, and rotation operates a differential gear. If the motor running from the taped signals changes speed, the differential gear cage turns. This operates a correction circuit which increases or reduces the tape motor speed. So movement of the tape is synchronized.

drum
picture—
244. Pictures by radio
screw
receiver

245. Synchronizing radio picture tape

picture tape
tape signal
crystal oscillator
tape motor
sync. motor
sync. motor
corrector
differential gear

127

thermocouple

amplifier and transmitter

decoder

voltage controlled tone oscillator

radio link

receiver

indicator

246. Radio telemetry for temperature information

Telemetry is conveying information from instruments to a recording device at a distance—for example, from a satellite to earth. One way is to convert the 'information' into an audio tone, which changes to convey data. As an example, a thermocouple produces a voltage which changes with temperature. This can be taken to an oscillator whose frequency changes with voltage. The tone is transmitted, picked up by a ground station, and decoded [246].

Satellites
Satellites can investigate conditions far above the earth, and send radio reports to ground stations. One employs an orthicon camera to take cloud pictures [247]. Pictures may be taken in daylight and are stored on tape in the satellite. When it is within range of a receiving station, the taped signals are radiated for decoding and printing.

A satellite can measure electron temperature, galactic radio noise, earth generated noise, oxygen density and other

247. Weather satellite

camera photographs' continental cloud cover

satellite radios pictures to ground station

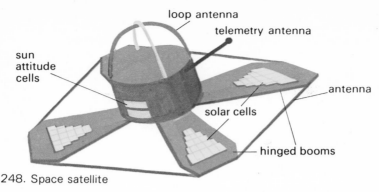

248. Space satellite

factors. In Figure 248 winged booms with solar cells produce current to operate internal equipment, and to charge storage batteries. Loop, extended and other antennas transmit and receive signals, to convey information to earth, or receive commands. Channels for radio signals are in the high frequency bands. Sun attitude cells receive illumination according to their bearing with relation to the sun's rays, and this can convey information on the tilt or rotation of the satellite.

A relay satellite can be situated thousands of miles above the earth, in a stationary orbit. Solar cells generate power. The satellite has antennas and equipment to receive transmissions, and re-transmit them on a frequency [249]. Transmissions are received on the ground by a large paraboloid dish, which reflects signals to a focus at a pick-up point. The efficiency of such dish parabolics is many thousands of times greater than that of an ordinary antenna and the receiver is specially designed for high sensitivity.

249. Radio relay by space satellite

Measurements in Electronic Circuits

Various measurements allow the working conditions of a circuit to be found. The simplest measurements are those which show a steady or uniform voltage or current.

A moving-coil meter winding is in a strong magnetic field, and receives current through hairsprings [250]. It turns slightly when current flows. This meter has a 'full scale deflection' or FSD of 6mA. A current of 6 milliamperes would move the pointer fully across the scale.

Current Through a Resistance = Voltage Divided by Resistance. So resistors in series with the meter allow various voltage ranges to be read.

Figure 251 has R1, R2 and R3 for ranges of 2.5 volts, 10 volts and 100 volts, and a 0.25mA meter. So R1 is 10,000 ohms; R2, 40,000 ohms; R3, 400,000 ohms.

To measure heavier currents we connect a resistor across the meter. Suppose $\frac{9}{10}$ of the total current flows through this resistor, and only $\frac{1}{10}$ through the meter [252]. The original range is multiplied 10 times.

The multi-range instrument in Figure 253 has a switch with nine positions.

250. The moving coil or d'arsonval meter—
basis of most test instruments

coil
hair
spring
pointer
magnet
assembly
center-
piece
pivot
adjuster

mA

At 1, R1 is in circuit for a voltage range. Positions 2, 3 and 4 give other voltage ranges. R2, R3 and R4 are in series, so that the higher voltages are not across a single resistor. Positions 6, 7, 8 and 9 move along a tapped shunt for higher current ranges. The shunt is permanently across the meter. Suppose the meter has a FSD of 0.5mA, or 1mA FSD with the shunt added. Then R1 is 2.5k for 2.5 volts, R2 is 10k for 10 volts, R3 is 90k for 100 volts (10k already present) and R4 is 150k for 250 volts (10k plus 90k already in the circuit).

251. Multipliers for voltage ranges

R1 R2 R3

−2·5V   10V   100V

test prods +

252. Parallel resistors or shunts

$\frac{1}{10}$th current—

$\frac{9}{10}$th current

10X original range

253. A multi-range meter circuit

254. Use of rectifier instrument

rectifier

meter indicates 'root mean square' value

AC input

pulsating DC output

Alternating Current

The moving coil cannot respond to AC. For AC ranges we add a rectifier [254] to a meter like that in Figure 250. This changes AC to pulsating DC. The meter shows the 'Root mean square' or effective value—what we generally need to know. 'Effective' value is that which has the same heating effect as equivalent direct current.

Resistances Too

We may need to measure resistance values. We use a battery, variable resistor VR, fixed resistor R, and the meter all in series [255]. We join test leads from the sockets together and adjust VR until the meter reads full scale. This is *zero ohms*. If we separate the test leads, no current flows, and the meter reads zero current, which is infinitely high resistance, or *infinity*. If we take the leads to a resistor, or circuit being tested, the meter will indicate some intermediate current, de-

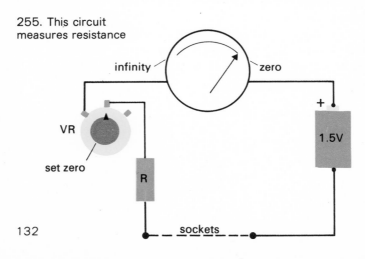

255. This circuit measures resistance

infinity

zero

VR

set zero

R

+

1.5V

sockets

pending on the resistance in the circuit. From Ohm's Law we can make a scale for the meter, showing resistance values.

A 'bridge' [256] permits accurate determination of resistance.

If $\frac{Ra}{Rb} = \frac{Rx}{Rc}$ there is no e.m.f. across the detector.

Rx is is the resistance to be measured and Rc an accurately calibrated variable resistor, or a decade box with values selected by switches. Ra and Rb are of known value or ratio. We find the value of Rx by noting what value of Rc produces no current at the detector.

256. Bridge measuring circuit

$$RX = \frac{RA}{RB} RC$$

Power Also

Power in Watts $= I^2R$ that is, *Current Squared* $\times$ *Resistance*. A known resistance in series with a meter allows watts to be found [257]. This is handy for some uses. Suppose R is 50 ohms and I is 2 amperes: $2 \times 2 \times 50 = 200$ watts.

Sometimes voltage drop across a resistance may be more readily found. Suppose R is a 2 ohm resistor replacing a loudspeaker and E proves to be 3 volts. From

$watts = \frac{E^2}{R} = \frac{3 \times 3}{2} = \frac{9}{2}$ we find that our amplifier is delivering 4.5 watts of audio power.

For direct current circuits, a DC meter is used. But for radio frequency, audio frequency, or alternating current circuits we must use a meter of appropriate type. Popular multi-range meters have scales, with range, AC/DC and ohms controls [258]. The switches bring into use the various parts of the circuit wanted.

257. Measuring power in watts

current I

resistance R

watts = $I^2 \times R$

volts V

resistance R

watts = $\dfrac{V^2}{R}$

258. Multi-range meter

scales

RANGE

ZERO

Millivoltmeters

A vacuum tube plate current changes with grid voltage. A plate meter can be calibrated in terms of voltage at the grid. Voltages to be tested are placed across a high value resistor R1 [259]. A range switch with resistors R1, R2, R3, etc. could be added.

A vacuum tube voltmeter allows extremely small voltages to be measured. The tube is very sensitive to grid voltage,

259. Vacuum tube voltmeter

tube

grid cap

meter

test points

R1

range switch

R1

R2

R3

grid

134

and so it has a cap for this connection, to avoid leakage.

Sensitive meter circuits are used to investigate exceedingly low voltages and currents, and to test circuits where current is too small for a moving-coil meter.

Sensitivity can be raised by using an amplifier [260]. V1 is the vacuum tube. Changes in plate current produce a change in voltage across R2. This voltage is taken across R3 to V2, so changing plate current through R4. With no input, VR1 is adjusted until the current through R5 is equal to that through R4, when the meter gives no reading. Low

260. VTVM with balanced amplifier

261. A transistor millivoltmeter

current or voltage at the 'Test Points' produces a reading on the meter. VR2 adjusts sensitivity.

The amplification from transistors allows sensitive measuring instruments to be made [261]. Here, a low voltage or current at 'Test' changes TR1 current, which flows through R1. This changes TR2 current through R2, which in turn changes TR3 current through R3. VR1 is first set for no reading, with no input. Zener diodes stabilize the emitter voltages of TR2 and TR3 because they maintain a certain voltage. The three transistors each amplify in series. Balanced circuits are often used to avoid errors due to transistors drifting.

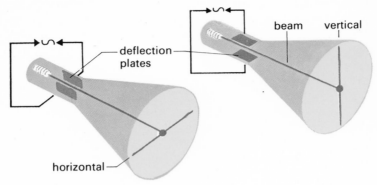

262. Use of oscilloscope for testing

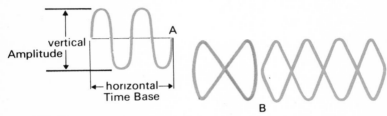

263. Traces on the scope screen

Oscilloscope

A cathode ray tube will display visually changes in current or voltage not shown by a meter. The cathode ray strikes the screen center, producing a bright spot [262]. Applying an alternating potential to the vertical plates deflects the beam up and down, making a vertical line. This deflection shows voltage amplitude. An alternating potential on the horizontal plates results in a horizontal line. By combining horizontal and vertical deflections we can display instantaneous events in a continuous pattern.

If we let an AC potential cause vertical scan, with horizontal scan from a sawtooth oscillator, we get a picture of the wave [263a]. Or we can take inputs to vertical and horizontal plates, causing wavy patterns in which the number of loops shows the relationship between one frequency and the other [263b].

136

The signals may need amplification [264]. Signals pass to the 'vertical amplifier' which raises the amplitude of weak inputs. The 'time base' is the generator of sawtooth waves, which sweep the spot across the screen. The 'sync' or synchronizing circuit takes a small part of the input signal and uses it to trigger the time-base, so that complicated traces remain stationary on the screen. A 'horizontal' amplifier is used. Another signal moves the spot horizontally. A 'power supply' provides current for each section, and for the tube, which may require 1,000 volts or more, at low current.

All sorts of phenomena can be displayed by the oscilloscope. For example, if an amplifier introduces third harmonic distortion, it combines with the fundamental frequency to produce an unpleasant result [265].

264. Cathode-ray oscilloscope

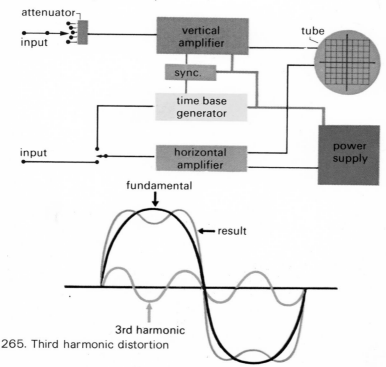

265. Third harmonic distortion

More Uses for Electronics

Electronics does remarkable things—if a process is wanted, an electronic circuit is usually possible.

Gasoline Pump

An electronic gas pump can replace the familiar electric pump. Coils on the pump are the windings for a low frequency oscillator [266], so the collector and coil current rise and fall. Valves in the piston and cylinder transform the rapid piston movement into a steady gasline pressure, exerted by a spring. This action provides a constant supply to the carburetor.

Interval Timer

An interval timer can automatically time a short period, and this can be repeated as often as is needed.

An electronic timer in Figure 267 makes use of the time constant of the large capacitor C. Transistor collector current holds the relay armature down. When the collector current falls, the armature is released. The potentiometer can be calibrated in seconds. Closing and opening of the relay contacts can control other apparatus.

Controlling Currents

The silicon-controlled rectifier or SCR can be turned on by applying current to a control electrode [268]. The SCR can deal with high power for motors and other appliances.

266. Transistorized gas pump   267. Transistorized interval timer
for vehicles

138

268. Silicon-controlled rectifier and circuit

269. Pulse width power control

plate

gate

cathode

gate input

starts conduction

controlled circuit

motor field coil

Zener diodes

rotor

shaded pole

DC supply

A

B +

pulse
C

D

E

270. Brushless direct current motor

A gate-controlled switch or GCS is somewhat similar in effect. The speed of a direct current electric motor can be reduced by a variable resistance in one conductor: voltage to the motor is less [269a]. This dissipates unused power as heat in the resistance. Another way is to employ a 'pulse width' oscillator to control a solid state rectifier which allows current to reach the motor. At [269b] current is present the whole time for full speed. In Figure 269c short 'off' intervals reduce the average motor current. In Figures 269d and 269e the 'off' intervals are longer, reducing speed further. No power is dissipated in heat.

Brushless DC Motor
The brushes of a DC motor can be noisy; they wear out, and the sparking may cause R-F interference. The brushless direct current motor employs power transistors to cause an oscillating current [270]. The motor has shaded pole windings, as used for an AC machine, and needs no brushes or commutator. R-F interference and sparking is eliminated.

139

diaphragm

midget transducer

sensing element

271. Transducers

Transducers and Ultrasonics

A 'transducer' supplies an electrical signal under the influence of pressure or other effects. A pressure transducer [271] alters its electrical resistance with changes in pressure, and so can operate a meter or other indicator. Microminiature pressure transducers have elements formed in silicon crystal, and may be fitted to engine parts, or even in the human body.

In ultrasonic flaw detection [272], steel bars or other materials tested receive the ultrasonic waves upon one surface. The bars may move through a tank, or the equipment may rest on the objects tested. The ultrasonic wave is re-

272. Ultrasonic flaw detection

ultrasonic generator

amplifier

display tube

transducer

top surface

bottom surface flaw

liquid

reflection

object tested

273. Electrolysis by passing a current in a chemical bath

274. Finding pH value of a liquid

flected by the more distant surface, and by internal flaws. A cathode ray tube shows the interval of time taken for the reflection, and thus whether a flaw is present.

Another use for ultrasonic equipment is in transmitting signals from a vessel into the water and receiving echoes from the sea bed, fish shoals, etc. The time for the echo to return depends on the distance. (See also page 126.)

Electro-Analysis

Various methods allow chemical analysis by electronic means. In electrolysis, compounds are chemically separated by the passage of an electric current. In the electrolysis of water, hydrogen escapes at the negative electrode, and oxygen at the positive electrode [273]. Ions migrating in the direction of the positive current are called cations, while those moving in the direction of the negative current are anions. Substances in solution may be deposited upon neutral electrodes, and afterward weighed.

The degree of acidity or pH value can be found by a sensitive instrument with immersed electrodes. One electrode is neutral and the other responds to the pH value, so the output from the electrodes depends on the latter. An extremely sensitive measuring circuit is needed [274].

141

More Semiconductor Effects

Gallium phosphide alloyed junction diodes and gallium arsenide diffused junction diodes produce light when current is passed in the forward or conducting direction. The gallium arsenide diode junction region has a high concentration of electrons and positive carriers. Photons are emitted when electrons change their energy level. The diode is a form of semiconductor laser or light amplifier—photons traveling along the junction region stimulate re-combination and extra photon emission, so producing more light [275].

Stimulation of a junction by light photons produces a current. A small-current diode may produce one electron for each photon [276]. In the avalanche silicon photo-diode, a potential is applied across the junction. The photons have a higher energy level, and more electrons are liberated. In the photo-transistor, the photo-diode junction forms the base-emitter elements, and transistor action amplifies the base current, so a larger collector current flows from a battery [276].

275. Light-producing diode

276. Photo-diodes and photo-transistor

photon

current

electron

photo-diode

avalanche photo-diode

photo-transistor

reflector

forward bias potential

The Field-Effect Transistor

This has source, gate and drain connections. It is P-channel or N-channel. Figure 277 is a field-effect transistor with a P-type gate in the N-type channel. Electron carriers flow from the source to the drain. Changing the gate voltage alters the current which can flow through channel and external circuit. With no gate potential, the channel is at maximum width, A. Current passes readily. With a small negative voltage at the gate, the channel is depleted of carriers, and therefore is smaller, B. Current is reduced. Increasing the voltage causes the channel to become narrower until it is 'pinched off' or scarcely able to conduct at all, C. The transistor has a high input resistance. It imposes a smaller load on a circuit that supplies the gate. Ordinary transistors are operated by the current flow at the base, and thus draw a current which loads the base circuit. The field-effect transistor is controlled by the voltage. Figure 278 is a field-effect transistor audio amplifier. This type of transistor is rapidly becoming more popular in radio and other equipment.

277. A field-effect transistor   278. F.E.T. amplifier circuit

Television Cameras

A television camera supplies a video signal, afterward amplified and radiated from a transmitter. As the whole scene cannot be changed simultaneously into electrical signals, it is 'scanned' or covered in regular lines. Covering the picture area constitutes a 'frame'. Frames follow each other with sufficient rapidity to avoid flickering at 30 frames per second.

A television picture is built up by a tiny spot of light from the cathode ray, which scans the screen rapidly. A television camera performs the reverse action, generating signals which correspond to the light and shade of the scene transmitted. With space vehicles, the impulses may be stored on tape, later used to supply the transmitter.

Figure 279 shows how a picture area is scanned or sampled by a moving area X of small size. During one frame, the small area X has covered the whole picture. (See the section on television receivers, page 88.)

A camera lens throws an image of the scene on a film [280]. A variable zoom lens, or interchangeable lenses, can give a choice of ordinary, wide-angle, close-up and other views.

279. Scanning of a picture image area

1st line
2nd line
3rd line

flyback to begin 2nd line

area so far covered

area to be covered

×

flyback to beginning of new frame

280. Formation of image by a convex lens

light rays

image

The image orthicon camera optical system projects an image on light-sensitive photocathode [281]. When light strikes the photocathode, photoelectrons are emitted from the other side. They are most numerous at bright areas of the image. An electric field attracts them to the target. This is extremely thin glass covered by a wire mesh having very many holes per square inch. The photoelectrons knock electrons from the glass, leaving a positive charge. So the positions and intensity of the positive charges correspond to light areas of the image.

The beam from an electron gun scans the back of the glass. When passing over an area where there is a positive charge, the beam leaves electrons to neutralize the charge. When the beam passes over an uncharged area, few if any of the electrons are left. Thus the beam current corresponds to light or dark picture features. An electron multiplier amplifies the changes in beam current. A series of electrodes receive progressively higher voltages [282]. Electrons striking these electrodes cause secondary electrons to be liberated, and the intensified signal can be passed on to other amplifiers.

281. Image orthicon used in TV camera

282. Electron multiplier

Logic Gates

Processes of logic can be carried out by 'gates' whose output depends on the logical process or 'truth' required. Computers use very many of these gates. Figure 283 is a 2-input AND gate. Input pulses arrive at A and B. Transistors 1 and 2 are normally non-conducting. There is no current through R1, no voltage drop here. Transistor 3 base is negative. Current flow through R2 causes a large voltage drop. Output level remains near zero (positive).

A pulse at A or B makes one transistor conduct, but no current flows in R1 unless *both* conduct simultaneously — that is, when pulses arrive at A *and* B together. Then voltage drop in R1 moves collector C positive, transistor 3 ceases to conduct, and a negative pulse appears in the output. Figure 284 is a 2-input OR gate. A pulse at either A OR B will cause an output pulse. Such units may operate at 500,000 pulses or more a second. They work with low voltage (typically 5 volts) and require little power.

283. A 2-input 'AND' gate and inverter

284. A 2-input 'OR' gate and inverter

285. Photocell or solar cell

286. Thermo-generator produces current from heat

Power in Space

Various unconventional ways of generating electrical power have been used in Polar weather stations, for automatic warning lights, satellites and space probes.

A convenient source of power for a space probe is the solar cell. Silicon solar cells have an N-type base containing antimony or other impurity, and a P-type surface layer. Photons or light from the sun striking the cell cause extra electron and hole pairs, and a current which flows through an external circuit [285]. This produces about 0.5 volt. The solar battery can charge accumulator-type cells, which provide power for equipment requiring more current and when the satellite is in darkness.

The thermo-generator is an improvement on the thermo-couple. In N-type material, electrons move away from a heat source. So a device can be made in which current is produced if one surface is hot, and the other cold [286]. The heat is a by-product of environment (solar) or of relevant activity. In a reverse or 'refrigeration' system the passage of an electric current makes a semi-conductor junction drop in temperature.

Looking Ahead

Analysis of gases, once needing considerable time, can be completed almost instantly. After ionization, the particles are accelerated down a drift tube [287]. Low mass ions accelerate most rapidly, so the ions are separated according to mass.

'Printed circuits' have revolutionized construction of miniature equipment. Conducting paths are arranged to run without overlapping. A large drawing is prepared, and reduced by photocopying methods. Further processing

287. High-speed spectrometer

leaves printed copper conductors [288]. Large numbers of similar panels are readily made. When components are fitted, the printed conductors act as wiring.

Printed circuits and similar methods lead to the production of modules, or small units of similar type. A defective unit is removed and replaced by one in working order.

Computers contain thousands of 'logic' elements, such as those for AND and OR functions. These and other circuit units can be tested automatically at high speed by a machine which applies suitable signals, and records the outputs [289]. Errors in outputs from the unit result in it being set aside for repair.

288. Underside of a printed circuit

foil conductors

289. Automated module testing

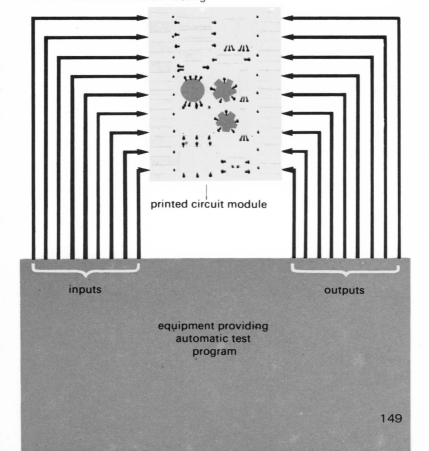

printed circuit module

inputs

outputs

equipment providing
automatic test
program

A Step Smaller

Even miniature individual resistors have wire ends and occupy unnecessary space. Instead, resistor material can be deposited directly on an insulated panel, between conductors [290]. The resistor has almost no thickness. If the process is carefully controlled, the resistors will be reasonably accurate in value. For high accuracy, the resistor is made a little low in value, and the value is increased by cutting or etching material away.

Conventional capacitors are of foil, separated by insulating paper; or have sheets of mica to separate the plates, or consist of conductive deposits on an insulator. Capacitors of almost no thickness are made [291]. Conducting layer A is deposited, then the insulator or dielectric B. A further conducting layer C is deposited on the insulator. Surfaces A and C form the capacitor.

Thin Films

In integrated circuits, the insulating base or panel is the substrate'. Surface roughness would result in irregular

290. Thin film resistors

long track

cuts

291. Thin film capacitors

plates

dielectric

C

B

A

292. Thin film resistor network

293. Thin film capacitors and equivalent circuit

deposits, so ceramic, glass, and other smooth substrates are used.

Resistors can be deposited nichrome, of extreme thinness, and resistance paths can be shaped as wanted, and tapped if required [292].

One method is to cover a prepared substrate chip with lacquer and photoresist, so that when the pattern is printed and etched the nichrome can afterward be deposited, giving the required thickness and shape.

Capacitors are made by vacuum depositing aluminum, then the dielectric (insulator), then aluminum again. The dielectric may be magnesium fluoride, zinc sulphide, silicon monoxide, or other material. For high capacities in small size, the film is very thin.

Deposits can be shaped to give the desired result. In Figure 293 the single conductor surface A is covered with dielectric B, then four top surfaces C, thus obtaining the equivalent of four capacitors.

151

294. Resistance capacitor network

dielectric film ⌐

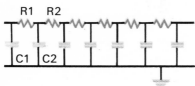

R1 R2

C1 C2

295. Semiconductor components

P layer⌐ resistor

N base⌐

N
P capacitor
N

full wave rectifier

Other Units

Figure 294 has a resistance element, then a dielectric or insulator. A film of conducting material is deposited on the insulator, so there is capacitance from it to the resistor throughout its length. This is approximately equivalent to a number of individual resistors R1, R2, etc. with small capacitors C1, C2, etc. Phase shift networks for oscillators and other purposes have been made in this way.

A completed integrated chip having resistors, capacitors and interconnecting conductors can be of extremely small size. The chip could be 0.1mm. thick, or less, and have many components in an area of a few square millimeters. A number of chips can be placed one on top of another, to build up a thicker unit, or cube, in which are many circuits.

Semiconductors Too

Semiconductor material can be fabricated into microminiature circuit elements. Silicon is preferred, for some increase in temperature is less important than it is with germanium.

A resistor is obtained by having a thin track of P-type material in the N-type base [295]. Capacitors can be derived by having N-type material separated by P-type material. Arrangements of suitably chosen material can provide more complicated circuit equivalents, such as the fullwave bridge rectifier.

Effects present in conventional semiconductor devices can be employed. In Figure 296 the variable capacitor has two metal plates, which are moved to change the capacitance. In the semiconductor variable capacitance diode, capacitance exists between the carrier areas. Applying a bias voltage effectively moves these areas together or apart, changing capacitance.

Planar transistors occupy little space and thickness. Another method adopted is shown in Figure 297. A base carries a resistance element acting as three resistors in series, with conductor strips A, B and C. Transistors are formed on the material. Input to X or Y will cause a voltage drop in R1, so that a pulse is obtained at B. This is a computer 'OR' gate.

296. Semiconductor variable capacitor

plates

P

N

P

N

space charge layer

297. Computer gate

X Y

A B C

X Y A

R1

B

C

153

Figure 298 is an integrated circuit formed by diffusion processes in a piece of semiconductor. With suitable external connections, it may form part of an amplifier, counter, oscillator, etc. With direct couplings and complementary circuits having PNP and NPN transistors, full use can be made of I.C. techniques.

298. Integrated microminiature circuit

299. Thin film multivibrator

out

C

Figure 299 is a thin film multivibrator or oscillator, which requires only the distributed capacitance resistor C for feedback, in conjunction with directly connected emitters.

Thin metal film resistors can be cut by electron beam. A powerful discharge tube produces a beam concentrated electromagnetically to a point 0.0005 in. in diameter. The beam is moved by magnetic deflection [300]. The process is carried out by automatic mechanisms [301].

It is interesting to imagine what electronics may accomplish in the future. A tidy picture of a central nucleus surrounded by negative electrons racing around at tremendous speed does well for many purposes. But much is still unknown. Many discoveries will be made.

300. Thin film resistors cut by electron beam

electronic gun

film before cutting —

electromagnetic lens

film after cutting—

cutting focus

301. Automated production of electronic units

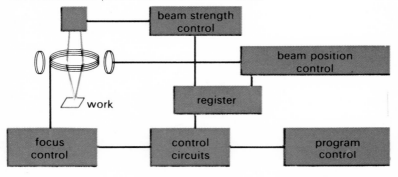

beam strength control

beam position control

register

work

focus control

control circuits

program control

GLOSSARY

Ampere: Unit of current.

Amplitude Modulation: Method of transmitting speech, etc.

Audio Amplifier: An amplifier which increases the strength of audible signals.

Auto-Transformer: One having tapped winding, instead of separate windings.

Bias: Usually steady voltage applied to establish operating point of vacuum tube.

Binary: Counting with 0 and 1 only.

Capstan: Rotating part causing steady movement of tape.

Cathode: Vacuum tube electrode emitting electrons; or semiconductor equivalent.

Class A: Amplification of the whole cycle.

Demodulation: Recovering the modulation or sound from a program.

Dielectric: Insulator (or air) between plates of a capacitor.

Dynamic Working: Actual operational working, as compared with static conditions.

Erasing (Tape): Restoring tape to original non-magnetized state.

Flip-Flop: Circuit which stays in either of two conditions.

Grid: Mesh electrode in tubes.

Grounded: Connected to ground, actually or effectively.

Harmonics: Vibrations or signals at multiples of original distortion.

Heater: Tube element heated by passage of current.

Heat Sink: Plate, etc. carrying away heat.

Henry: Unit of inductance.

Hertz: Unit of frequency.

Inductor: Coil, etc. possessing inductance.

Logic Gate: Circuit which performs an operation in logic.

Module: Small or standard unit.

Multivibrator: Type of oscillator.

Non-Inductive: Resistor, etc. designed to avoid effects of inductance.

Ohm: Unit of resistance.

Optimum Load: Best working load for a transistor, tube or other device.

Oscilloscope: Instrument which displays waveforms, etc. on cathode ray tube screen.

Plate: Vacuum tube electrode normally receiving positive 'B' supply.

Polarization (Antenna): Vertical or horizontal placement of elements.

Radar: Radio Detection And Ranging.

Rectifier: Device allowing current to pass easily in one direction only.

Resonance: Natural oscillation frequency of a circuit, etc.

Scanning: Regular motion to take in an arranged area.

Sonar: Sound Navigation And Ranging.

Stage: One unit or section of amplifier, etc.

Telemetry: Relaying instrument information to a distance.

Ultrasonics: Operating methods beyond the range of hearing.

Watt: Unit of power.

INDEX

Page numbers in bold type
refer to illustrations

OTHER TITLES IN THE SERIES

The GROSSET ALL-COLOR GUIDES provide a library of authoritative information for readers of all ages. Each comprehensive text with its specially designed illustrations yields a unique insight into a particular area of man's interests and culture.

NOW AVAILABLE

PREHISTORIC ANIMALS
BIRD BEHAVIOR
WILD CATS
FOSSIL MAN
PORCELAIN
MILITARY UNIFORMS, 1686–1918
BIRDS OF PREY
FLOWER ARRANGING
MICROSCOPES & MICROSCOPIC LIFE
THE PLANT KINGDOM
ROCKETS & MISSILES
FLAGS OF THE WORLD
ATOMIC ENERGY
WEATHER & WEATHER FORECASTING
TRAINS
SAILING SHIPS & SAILING CRAFT
ELECTRONICS
MYTHS & LEGENDS OF ANCIENT GREECE
CATS, HISTORY—CARE—BREEDS
DISCOVERY OF AFRICA
HORSES & PONIES
FISHES OF THE WORLD
ASTRONOMY
SNAKES OF THE WORLD
DOGS, SELECTION—CARE—TRAINING

SOON TO BE PUBLISHED